National 5
Chemistry
Practice Papers for SQA Exams

Barry McBride

Contents

The instructions and answer grid for completion of Section 1 in each practice paper can be downloaded from www.hoddereducation.co.uk/updatesandextras.

HODDER GIBSON
AN HACHETTE UK COMPANY

The Publishers would like to thank the following for permission to reproduce copyright material:

Photo credits p.71 © Medtronic (www.medtronicacademy.com).

Acknowledgements Exam rubrics at the start of each practice paper Copyright © Scottish Qualifications Authority; Text extract on p.43 adapted from www.rsc.org/chemistryworld/2015/07/philae-poses-comet-chemistry-conundrum; Text extract on p.70 adapted from www.compoundchem.com/2013/12/30/the-chemistry-of-fireworks/.

Every effort has been made to trace all copyright holders, but if any have been inadvertently overlooked the Publishers will be pleased to make the necessary arrangements at the first opportunity.

Although every effort has been made to ensure that website addresses are correct at time of going to press, Hodder Gibson cannot be held responsible for the content of any website mentioned in this book. It is sometimes possible to find a relocated web page by typing in the address of the home page for a website in the URL window of your browser.

Hachette UK's policy is to use papers that are natural, renewable and recyclable products and made from wood grown in sustainable forests. The logging and manufacturing processes are expected to conform to the environmental regulations of the country of origin.

Orders: please contact Bookpoint Ltd, 130 Park Drive, Milton Park, Abingdon, Oxon OX14 4SE. Telephone: (44) 01235 827720. Fax: (44) 01235 400454. Lines are open 9.00–5.00, Monday to Saturday, with a 24-hour message answering service. Visit our website at www.hoddereducation.co.uk. Hodder Gibson can be contacted direct on: Tel: 0141 333 4650; Fax: 0141 404 8188; email: hoddergibson@hodder.co.uk

© Barry McBride 2016
First published in 2016 by
Hodder Gibson, an imprint of Hodder Education,
An Hachette UK Company
211 St Vincent Street
Glasgow G2 5QY

Impression number   5 4 3 2 1
Year   2020 2019 2018 2017 2016

Cover photo © ssilver/123RF.com
Illustrations by Aptara, Inc.
Typeset in India by Aptara, Inc.
Printed and bound by CPI Group (UK) Ltd, Croydon, CR0 4YY

A catalogue record for this title is available from the British Library

ISBN: 978 1 4718 8342 2

Introduction

National 5 Chemistry

The course

Before sitting your National 5 Chemistry examination, you must have passed three Unit Assessments within your school or college.

To achieve a pass in National 5 Chemistry there are then two further main components.

Component 1: the assignment

You are required to submit an assignment that is worth 20% (20 marks) of your final grade. This will be based on research and may include an experiment. The assignment will require you to apply skills, knowledge and understanding to investigate a relevant topic in chemistry and its effect on the environment and/or society. Your school or college will provide you with a guide for this assignment which has been produced by the SQA. This guide gives information on what is required to complete the report and gain as many marks as possible.

Your assignment report will be marked by the SQA.

Component 2: the question paper

The question paper will assess breadth and depth of knowledge and understanding from across all of the three units.

The question paper will require you to:

- make statements, provide explanations and describe information to demonstrate knowledge and understanding
- apply knowledge and understanding to new situations to solve problems
- plan and design experiments
- present information in various forms such as graphs, tables, etc.
- perform calculations based on information given
- give predictions or make generalisations based on information given
- draw conclusions based on information given
- suggest amendments to experiments to improve the accuracy of results obtained or to improve safety.

To achieve a C grade in National 5 Chemistry you must achieve at least 50% of the 100 marks available when the two components, the question paper and the assignment, are combined. For a B grade you will need 60%, while for an A grade you must ensure that you gain as many of the marks available as possible and at least 70%.

This book contains practice papers that cover the content of the National 5 Chemistry course and illustrate the standard, structure and requirements of the question paper that you will sit during the exam.

Each practice paper consists of two sections. (A detailed marking scheme for each section is provided at the end of this book.)

- Section 1 will contain objective questions (multiple choice) and will be worth 20 marks.
- Section 2 will contain restricted- and extended-response questions and will be worth 60 marks.

Each practice paper contains a variety of questions including questions that require:

- a demonstration of, and application of, knowledge and understanding of the mandatory content of the course from across the three units
- the application of scientific inquiry skills.

How to use this book

This book can be used in two ways:

1   You can complete an entire practice paper under exam conditions, without the use of books or notes, then mark the paper using the marking scheme provided. This method gives you a clear indication of the level you are working at and should highlight the content areas that you need to work on before attempting the next practice paper. Using this method enables you to see your progress as you complete each practice paper.

2   You can complete a practice paper using your notes and books. Try the question first and then refer to your notes if you are unable to answer it. The detailed marking scheme also provides information to help you understand the answers given. This is a form of studying and by doing this you will be covering all the areas of content that you are weakest in. You should notice that you are referring to your notes less with each practice paper completed.

The revision grid on page 7 allows you to target a specific area of the course. If, for example, you feel that you need to concentrate more on radiation, then the grid will list all the questions based on radiation across the three papers.

Try to practise as many questions as possible. This will help you become familiar with the language used in the question papers and ultimately improve your chances of success.

You are now ready to begin the practice papers. At the start of Section 1 and Section 2 of each practice paper, we have provided instructions on how to fill in your answers, similar to what you will read in your exam paper. Please be aware that the instructions have been adjusted to be more suitable for the revision purposes of this book, but are aimed at preparing you for the final exam. Please visit www.hoddereducation.co.uk/updatesandextras to download full instructions on how to answer Section 1 multiple choice questions and there is an answer grid for you to practise with.

Hints and tips

Below is a list of hints and tips that will help you to achieve your full potential in the National 5 exam:

- Make sure you **read each question carefully**. Scanning the question and missing the main points results in mistakes being made. Some students highlight the main points of a question with a highlighter pen to ensure that they don't miss anything out.
- Open-ended questions will include the statement, '**Using your knowledge of chemistry**'. These questions provide you with an opportunity to 'show off' your chemistry knowledge. To obtain the 3 marks on offer for these questions you must demonstrate a good understanding of the chemistry involved and provide a logically correct answer to the question posed. There is no single correct answer for the open-ended questions. Listed in the marking scheme are *some* of the options that may be included and explained in your answer. This list is not exhaustive and you do not have to include all of these to gain the full 3 marks. Ensure that what you have included has been explained fully and clearly. Include diagrams and equations that may help with your explanation.
- When doing questions involving calculations, ensure that you **show all your working**. If you make a simple arithmetical mistake you may still be awarded some of the marks but *only* if your working is laid out clearly so that the examiner can see where you went wrong. Just giving the answer is very risky; you won't receive any credit for your answer if it is wrong.
- In every National 5 Chemistry exam, there is 1 extra mark available for providing the correct unit for a calculation, for example $cm^3 s^{-1}$. Most calculations will provide the unit in the question such as '*Calculate the mass, in grams, of ...*', but there is always one calculation without a unit. If you provide the correct unit in this case, you will receive an extra mark.
- **Attempt all questions.** Leaving a question blank means that you will definitely not gain any marks for it.
- When you are required to read a passage to answer a question, make sure you **read it carefully** as the information you require is contained within it. It may not be obvious at first but the answers will be contained within the passage.
- If a question asks you to 'explain', then you must **explain your answer fully**. For example, if you are asked to explain how a covalent bond holds atoms together, you cannot simply say:

  '*A covalent bond is a shared pair of electrons between non-metal atoms.*' This answer tells the examiner what a covalent bond is but does not explain how it holds the atoms together. To gain the marks an answer similar to the following should be written:

  '*A covalent bond is a shared pair of electrons between non-metal atoms. The shared electrons are attracted to the nuclei of both atoms which creates a tug-of-war effect, resulting in a covalent bond.*'
- You will be required to draw a graph in most exams. To obtain all the marks, ensure that the graphs have **labels**, **units** and **points plotted correctly**. Make sure you use suitable scales so that the graph fills most of the graph paper provided.

- **Use your data booklet**. When you are asked to write formulae, ionic formulae, formula mass, etc., look up the numbers you require in the data booklet. It would be a good idea to familiarise yourself with the contents of the data booklet *before* the exam, then you will know exactly what information can be found within it.
- Work on your **timing**. The multiple-choice section (Section 1) should take approximately 30 minutes. Attempt to answer the multiple-choice questions before you look at the four possible answers, as this will improve your confidence. Use scrap paper when required to scribble down structural formulae, calculations, chemical formulae, and so on; this will reduce your chance of making errors. If you are finding the question difficult, try to eliminate the obviously wrong answers to increase your chances.
- When asked to **predict or estimate** based on information from a graph or a table, take your time to look for patterns. For example, if asked to predict a boiling point, try to establish whether there is a regular change in boiling point and use that regular pattern to establish the unknown boiling point.
- When drawing a **diagram** of an experiment, ask yourself the question, 'Would this work if I set it up exactly like this in the lab?' Ensure that the method you have drawn would produce the desired results *safely*. If, for example, you are heating a flammable reactant such as alcohol, then you will not gain the marks if you heat it with a Bunsen burner; a water bath would be much safer! Make sure your diagram is labelled clearly.

Remember that the rewards for passing National 5 Chemistry are well worth it! Your pass will help you get the future you want for yourself. In the exam, be confident in your own ability. If you are not sure how to answer a question, trust your instincts and just give it a go anyway. Keep calm and don't panic.

Good luck!

Revision grid

Key area	Paper A		Paper B		Paper C		Date to complete
	Section 1	Section 2	Section 1	Section 2	Section 1	Section 2	
Unit 1							
Rates of reaction		1 a), 1 b), 12 b) (iii)		5 a), 5 b)	4	12 a) (i), 12 a) (ii), 12 b) (i), 12 b) (ii)	
Atomic structure and bonding related to properties of materials	1, 2, 3, 4, 5, 6, 7, 8, 10	10 a), 10 b), 10 c) (i), 10 c) (ii), 12 a) (ii)	2, 3, 4	1 b) (i), 1 b) (ii), 9 c) (ii), 13 b) (ii)	1, 2, 3	1 a) (i), 1 a) (ii), 1 b), 4 b), 8 b) (ii)	
Formulae and reaction quantities	9	1 c) (ii), 3 c) (ii), 6 b) (ii), 12 c) (i)	5, 7, 8	1 c), 9 c) (i), 13 b) (i)	5, 13	2 a), 10 b)	
Acids and bases	11	12 b) (i)	6	13 a)	6, 7		
Neutralisation reactions	18	8 a), 8 b)		2 b) (ii)	8	8 a), 11 b) (i), 11 b) (ii)	
Unit 2							
Homologous series	12, 14	4 c), 11 b)	9, 10	3 c) (i), 12 c)	9, 11, 12	7 c)	
Alcohols	13	7 c) (i)	12	6 a) (i), 6 a) (ii)		7 b) (i)	
Carboxylic acids		7 a), 7 b)		2 a) (i), 2 a) (ii), 2 b) (i)		7 b) (ii), 11 a)	
Esters		7 c) (ii)	13	8 a), 12 a)		7 a)	
Energy from fuels		1 c) (i), 4 b)		6 b), 6 c), 6 d)	14	9 b), 9 c)	
Unit 3							
Metals	15, 16, 17	6 a), 6 b) (i)	15, 16, 18	1 a) (i), 1 a) (ii), 9 a), 9 b)	15, 16, 17	8 b) (i), 10 a), 10 c) (i), 10 c) (ii)	
Properties of plastics	20	11 a)	17	8 b), 8 c)	18	13 a), 13 b) (i), 13 b) (ii)	

Fertilisers		3 a), 3 c) (i), 12 a) (i)		11 a), 11 b) (i), 11 b) (ii), 11 c)	19	4 a), 4 d) (i), 4 d) (ii)	
Nuclear chemistry		9 a), 9 b), 9 c)	14	10 a), 10 b), 10 c) (i), 10 c) (ii)	20	1 c), 6 a) (i), 6 a) (ii)	
Chemical analysis	19	12 c) (ii)	19, 20	5 c)		2 c), 9 a)	
Open questions	2 and 5		4 and 7		3 and 5		
Problem-solving type		3 b), 3 d), 4 a), 10 c) (iii), 12 b) (ii)	1, 11	3 a), 3 b), 3 c) (ii), 12 b) (i), 12 b) (ii), 13 b) (iii)	10	2 b), 2 d), 4 c) (i), 4 c) (ii), 6 b), 8 c)	

National 5 Chemistry

Section 1

1 Which of the following elements exists as a covalent molecule?

   A Neon

   B Silicon

   C Oxygen

   D Magnesium

2 An atom has an atomic number of 11 and a mass number of 23.

The atom has

   A 11 protons and 12 neutrons

   B 11 protons and 23 neutrons

   C 12 protons and 11 neutrons

   D 23 protons and 11 neutrons.

3 Which of the following particles is an ion?

Particle	Protons	Electrons	Neutrons
A	19	19	20
B	7	7	14
C	17	17	35
D	8	10	16

4 The shape of a methane molecule is shown below.

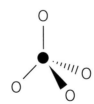

Which of the following compounds would have molecules with the same shape as a methane molecule?

   A Water

   B Ammonia

   C Carbon dioxide

   D Carbon tetrafluoride

5 Two stable atoms of hydrogen exist.

$^{1}_{1}H$ and $^{2}_{1}H$

What term can be used to describe these atoms?

A Isomers

B Isotopes

C Diatomic

D Saturated

6 What is the charge on the titanium ion in $TiBr_3$?

A 1+

B 1−

C 3+

D 3−

Questions 7 and 8 refer to the table below.

The table contains information about four substances.

Substance	Melting point/°C	Boiling point/°C	Conducts as a solid	Conducts as a liquid
A	−9	21	No	No
B	650	1090	Yes	Yes
C	1414	3265	No	No
D	714	1412	No	Yes

7 Identify the substance which is a liquid at 20 °C.

8 Identify the substance that exists as an ionic lattice.

9 0.1 mol of a gas has a mass of 4.4 g.

Which of the following could be the molecular formula of the gas?

A NH_3

B CO_2

C H_2O

D SO_2

10 Ionic substances conduct electricity in solution because

A the electrons are free to move

B the ions are free to move

C all liquids conduct electricity

D there are no charged particles in ionic solutions.

11 Which of the following oxides would dissolve in water, resulting in a solution with a pH greater than 7?

    A   Sulfur dioxide

    B   Carbon dioxide

    C   Potassium oxide

    D   Magnesium oxide

12

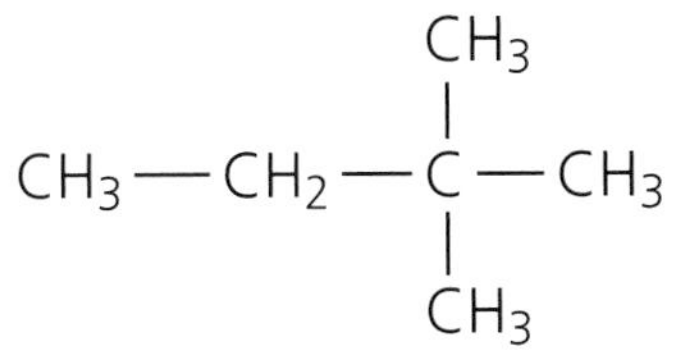

The name of the above compound is

    A   1,2-dimethylbutane

    B   2,2-dimethylbutane

    C   3,3-dimethylbutane

    D   2,1-dimethylbutane.

13 Which of the following compounds is an alcohol?

    A C_2H_5OH

    B $C_2H_5OC_2H_5$

    C C_2H_5COOH

    D $C_2H_5OOCCH_3$

14 Three members of the dienes homologous series are

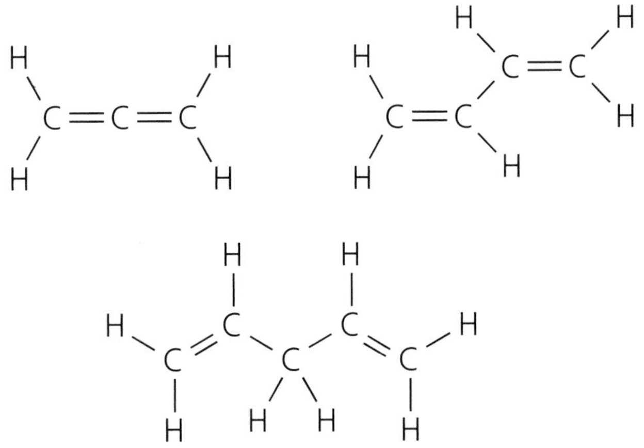

Which of the following is the general formula for this homologous series?

    A C_nH_{2n+2}

    B C_nH_{2n}

    C C_nH_{2n-2}

    D C_nH_{2n-4}

15 $Zn^{2+} + 2e^- \rightarrow Zn$

This ion–electron equation represents

A reduction of zinc(II) ions
B reduction of zinc(I) ions
C oxidation of zinc(II) ions
D oxidation of zinc(I) ions.

16 Which of the following metals is obtained from its ore by electrolysis?

A Iron
B Copper
C Silver
D Aluminium

17 Four cells were made by connecting copper, tin, aluminium and iron to silver as shown.

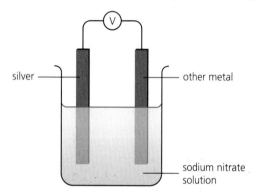

silver — other metal

sodium nitrate solution

Which line in the table shows the voltage of the cell produced by connecting aluminium to silver?

	Voltage/V
A	0.4
B	0.6
C	0.9
D	1.4

Questions 18 and 19 refer to the equation for the reaction between sodium iodide solution and silver nitrate solution shown below.

$$NaI(aq) + AgNO_3(aq) \rightarrow NaNO_3(aq) + AgI(s)$$

18 The spectator ions in this reaction are

A Ag^+ and I^-
B Ag^+ and NO_3^-
C Na^+ and I^-
D Na^+ and NO_3^-.

19 The type of reaction represented by the equation is

    A   neutralisation

    B   precipitation

    C   condensation

    D   displacement.

20 Part of a structure of a polymer is shown below.

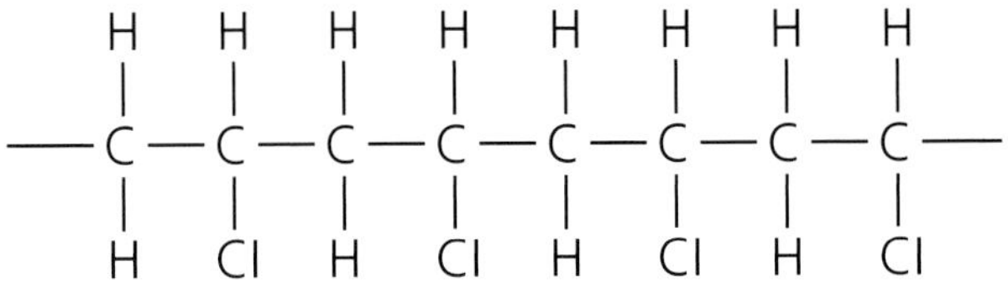

The monomer used to make this polymer is

A

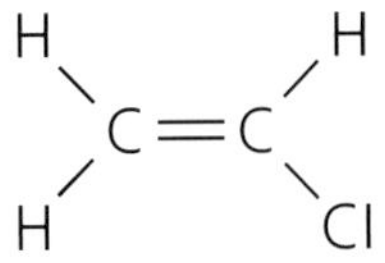

B

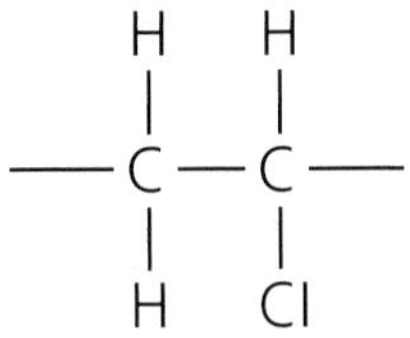

C

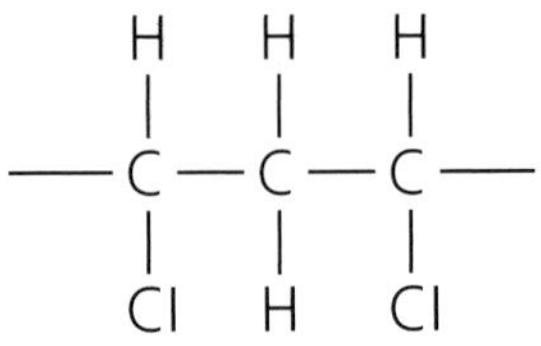

D

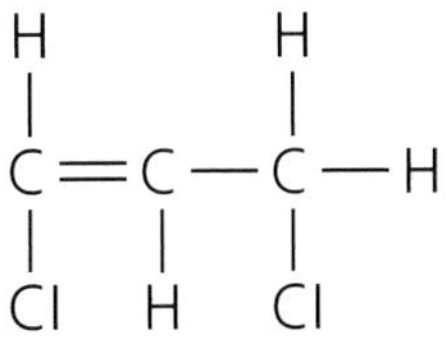

[End of Section 1]

Section 2

Total marks: 60

Attempt ALL questions.

Write your answers clearly in the spaces provided in this paper. Additional space for answers and rough work is provided at the end of this paper. If you use this space you must clearly identify the question number you are attempting. Any rough work must be written in this space. You should score through your rough work when you have written your final copy.

MARKS

1   Many, but not all, metals react with acid. Hydrogen gas is formed as the metal reacts with the acid to form a salt.

Performing the experiment shown allows the rate of the reaction to be monitored.

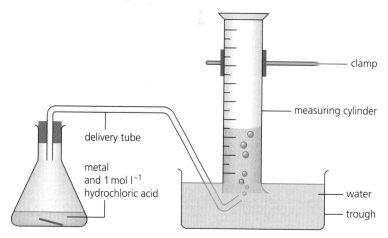

The results below were produced when magnesium metal was used.

Time/s	0	20	40	60	80	100	120	140
Volume of hydrogen/cm³	0	30	51	65	74	78	80	80

a) Draw a line graph of the results.
Use appropriate scales to fill most of the paper.

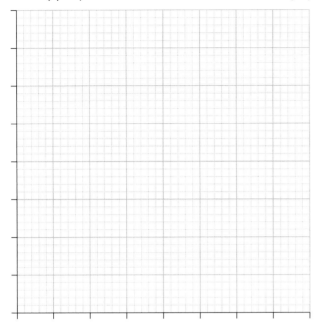

b) **(i)** Calculate the average rate of reaction between 40 and 80 seconds.
Your answer must include the appropriate unit.
Show your working clearly.

(ii) The rate of the reaction decreases as the reaction progresses.
Suggest a reason for this.

c) **(i)** The temperature of the reaction mixture increased as the reaction proceeded.
What name is given to a reaction that releases heat?

(ii) Write the formula equation for the reaction between magnesium and hydrochloric acid. (There is no need to balance the equation.)

A

2 The phrase 'opposites attract' can be used to describe relationships.

Using your knowledge of chemistry, suggest how this term is also relevant to chemistry.

National 5 Chemistry

3 Read the passage and answer the questions which follow.

> Nitrous oxide (N_2O) is naturally present in the atmosphere as part of the Earth's nitrogen cycle, and has a variety of natural sources. However, human activities such as agriculture are increasing the amount of N_2O in the atmosphere.
>
> Nitrous oxide contributes to both global warming and depletion of the ozone layer and is believed to be the third largest contributor to global warming after carbon dioxide and methane. A recent study has suggested that emissions of the gas from agriculture have been underestimated by 40%.
>
> As part of the study, scientists monitored the concentration of nitrous oxide in numerous rivers and tributaries and the results confirmed that there had been a large increase in the concentration of the substance found in these water systems.
>
> The factors that significantly influence agricultural N_2O emissions mainly concern agricultural practices such as application rate, crop type, fertiliser type and soil conditions. One way of reducing the emissions of nitrous oxide is to improve the efficiency of the use of nitrogen as a fertiliser because at present only 50% of the nitrogen applied through fertilisers is actually used by the plant.

MARKS

a) Why are fertilisers added to soil?   1

b) Which three gases are the biggest contributors to climate change?   1

c) **(i)** Ammonium nitrate, NH_4NO_3, is an important fertiliser. Calculate the percentage, by mass, of nitrogen in ammonium nitrate.
Show your working clearly.   3

MARKS

(ii) Write the ionic formula of ammonium nitrate. 1

d) If a farmer applied 1000 kg of a nitrogen fertiliser to a field, how much of it would be used by the plants? 1

4 The higher the octane number of a fuel, the more efficient the fuel is.

The octane numbers for some hydrocarbons are shown in the table.

Hydrocarbon	Number of carbon atoms	Octane number
Butane	4	90
Pentane	5	55
Hexane	6	25
Heptane	7	0
Octane	8	

a) **(i)** Predict the octane number of octane.

1

(ii) State a relationship between the number of carbon atoms in a hydrocarbon and its efficiency as a fuel.

1

b) A student investigated the amount of energy released when hexane was burned. The student recorded the following data.

Mass of hexane burned	2.5 g
Volume of water	500 cm³
Initial temperature of water	20 °C
Final temperature of water	49 °C
Specific heat capacity of water	4.18 kJ kg⁻¹ °C⁻¹

Calculate the energy released in kJ.

Show your working clearly.

3

c) Iso-octane (2,2,4-trimethylpentane) is commonly used as a fuel because it has an octane rating of 100.

(i) Draw the full structural formula of iso-octane.

MARKS

1

(ii) Iso-octane is an isomer of octane.

State what is meant by the term isomer.

1

5 The concentration of ethanoic acid contained in bottles of vinegar varies from brand to brand.

Using your knowledge of chemistry, describe a method that could be used to establish which brand of vinegar contains the highest concentration of ethanoic acid.

3

6 Iron can be extracted from magnetite, a naturally occurring iron compound, in a blast furnace.

a) State the term used to describe naturally occurring metal compounds such as magnetite.

1

b) (i) Magnetite contains iron(III) ions which are reduced to produce the iron metal.

Write the ion–electron equation for this reaction.

1

(ii) The overall reaction that takes place in the blast furnace is shown by the equation

$$Fe_2O_3 + 3CO \rightarrow 2Fe + 3CO_2$$

Calculate the mass, in grams, of iron produced when 1000 g of iron oxide reacts with carbon monoxide.

Show your working clearly.

3

7   Formic acid (methanoic acid) is found in the venom of fire ants.

The structure of formic acid is shown.

a)   Name the functional group present in formic acid.

b)   Explain why formic acid is soluble in water.

Formic acid can be used to produce esters.

c)   (i)   Name the type of compound that would react with formic acid to produce an ester.

(ii) Suggest a use for the ester produced in this reaction.

8   A student carried out titrations to establish the concentration of a sodium
    hydroxide solution using the apparatus below.

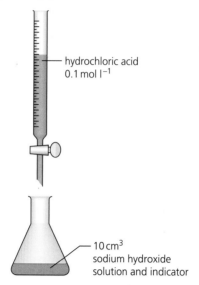

hydrochloric acid
0.1 mol l^{-1}

10 cm^3
sodium hydroxide
solution and indicator

The results of the titrations are given in the table.

Titration	Initial burette reading/cm³	Final burette reading/cm³	Total/cm³
1	0.0	15.9	15.9
2	15.9	31.0	15.1
3	31.0	45.9	14.9

a)   Calculate the average volume of acid, in cm³, that should be used in
     calculating the concentration of the sodium hydroxide solution.

1

b)   The equation for the reaction is

$$HCl(aq) + NaOH(aq) \rightarrow NaCl(aq) + H_2O(l)$$

Calculate the concentration, in mol l^{-1}, of the sodium hydroxide solution.
Show your working clearly.

3

9 Americium-241, a radioisotope used in household smoke detectors, is an alpha-emitting isotope.

a) What is meant by the term isotope?

1

b) Write a balanced nuclear equation for the alpha decay of $^{241}_{95}Am$.

1

c) Americium-241 has a half-life of 433 years.
State what is meant by the term half-life?

1

10 Atoms contain particles called protons, neutrons and electrons.

MARKS

The nuclide notation of a potassium atom is shown.

$$^{39}_{19}K$$

a) Complete the table to show the number of each type of particle in
this potassium atom.

1

Particle	Number
Electrons	19
Protons	
Neutrons	

b) Atoms can lose or gain electrons to form ions.
Explain why atoms form ions?

1

c) Electrons can be removed from all atoms. The energy required to do
this is called the first ionisation energy.

The first ionisation energy is the energy required to remove one mole of
electrons from one mole of atoms in the gaseous state.

The equation for the first ionisation energy of potassium is

$$K(g) \rightarrow K^+(g) + e^-$$

(i) Complete the diagram to show how the electrons are arranged
in a potassium **ion**.

1

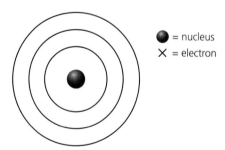

● = nucleus
X = electron

(ii) Explain what holds the negatively charged electrons in place around
the nucleus.

1

(iii) Write the ion–electron equation for the first ionisation energy
of magnesium.

1

11 Cyanoacrylates are a family of strong, fast-acting adhesives with industrial, medical and household uses. The structure of cyanoacrylate is shown.

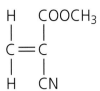

a) **(i)** Cyanoacrylate forms a polymer by combining with other cyanoacrylate molecules.

Name the type of polymerisation that would take place between cyanoacrylate monomers.

1

(ii) Draw the repeating unit of the polymer formed.

1

b) Describe the chemical test that you would use, including the expected result, to show that cyanoacrylate is unsaturated.

1

12 Below is a flow diagram of the Ostwald process, which is used to manufacture nitric acid.

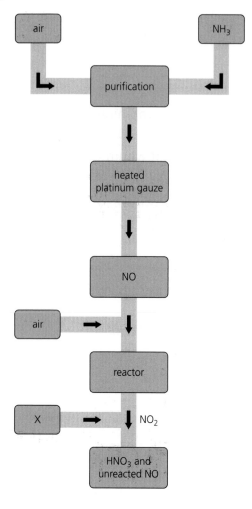

a) (i) Name the industrial process which is used to manufacture ammonia.

1

(ii) Draw a diagram to show how all the outer electrons are arranged in an ammonia molecule.

1

b) (i) Name substance X from the flow diagram.

1

(ii) **On the flow diagram**, draw an arrow to show how the process could be made more economical.

1

(iii) The Ostwald process uses a platinum catalyst.
Suggest why a catalyst may be used in an industrial process.

1

c) The nitric acid can be used to produce the fertiliser calcium nitrate.

$$HNO_3(aq) + Ca(OH)_2(aq) \rightarrow Ca(NO_3)_2(aq) + H_2O(l)$$

(i) Balance the equation shown.

1

(ii) State how a **solid** sample of calcium nitrate could be obtained from the calcium nitrate solution.

1

[End of Section 2]
[END OF PRACTICE PAPER A]

ADDITIONAL SPACE FOR ANSWERS AND ROUGH WORK

Additional graph paper for Question 1 a)

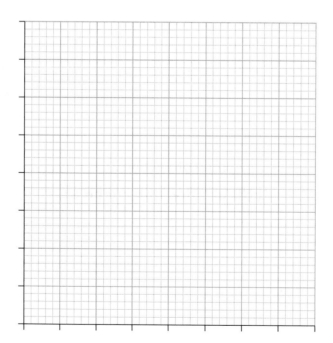

ADDITIONAL SPACE FOR ANSWERS AND ROUGH WORK

National 5 Chemistry

Section 1

Total marks: 20

Attempt ALL questions. Answer grid available at www.hoddereducation.co.uk/updatesandextras.

1   Which of the following elements was discovered **before** 1808?

   A   Barium

   B   Calcium

   C   Magnesium

   D   Potassium

2   Which of the following is the electron arrangement of a halogen?

   A   2,8,1

   B   2,8,2

   C   2,8,7

   D   2,8,8

3   Which of the following has a covalent molecular structure?

   A   Neon

   B   Silicon dioxide

   C   Calcium chloride

   D   Carbon dioxide

4   The shape of an ammonia molecule is shown below.

What name is given to describe the shape of an ammonia molecule?

   A   Linear

   B   Angular

   C   Trigonal pyramidal

   D   Tetrahedral

5   What is the charge on the titanium ion in TiO?

   A   1+

   B   2+

   C   1−

   D   2−

6 Which of the following oxides can be described as a base?

- **A** Sodium oxide
- **B** Sulfur dioxide
- **C** Silicon dioxide
- **D** Sodium sulfate

7 $xN_2(g) + yH_2(g) \rightarrow zNH_3(l)$

This equation will be balanced when

- **A** $x = 1$, $y = 2$ and $z = 1$
- **B** $x = 1$, $y = 3$ and $z = 1$
- **C** $x = 1$, $y = 3$ and $z = 2$
- **D** $x = 2$, $y = 3$ and $z = 2$.

8 0.1 mol of a gas has a mass of 4.6 g.

Which of the following could be the molecular formula for the gas?

- **A** SO_2
- **B** CO_2
- **C** NO_2
- **D** O_2

9 Which of the following could be the molecular formula of cycloalkane?

- **A** C_4H_4
- **B** C_4H_6
- **C** C_4H_8
- **D** C_4H_{10}

10

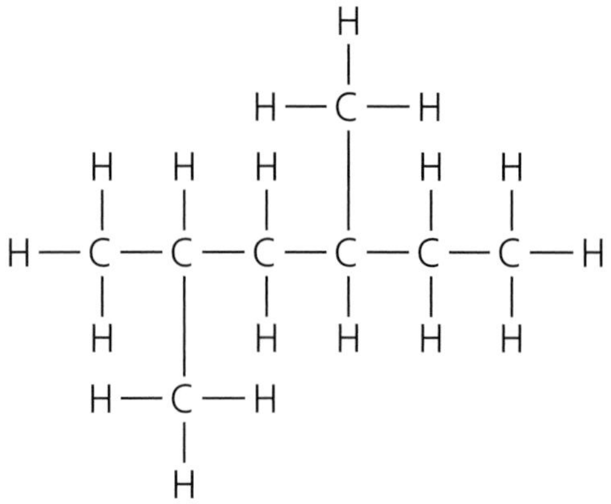

The name of the above compound is

- **A** 2,4-methylhexane
- **B** 2,4-dimethylhexane
- **C** 3,5-methylheptane
- **D** 2,4-dimethylheptane.

11 The first three members of the alkyne homologous series are shown.

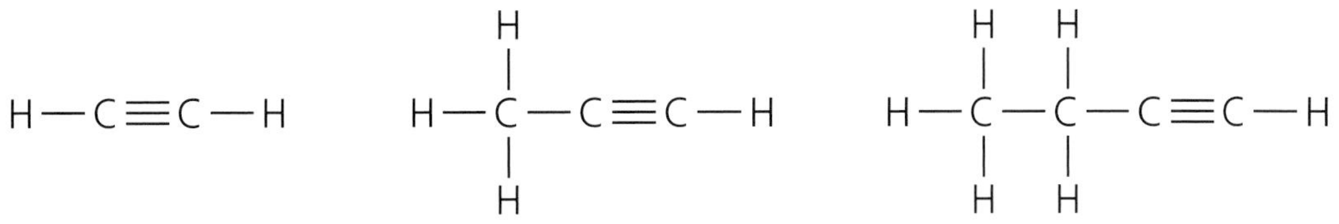

$$H-C\equiv C-H$$

H−C≡C−H, H−C(H)(H)−C≡C−H, H−C(H)(H)−C(H)(H)−C≡C−H

Which of the following is the general formula of the alkynes?

A C_nH_{2n+2}

B C_nH_{2n}

C C_nH_{2n-2}

D C_nH_{2n-3}

12 Which of the following can be classed as an alcohol?

A CH_3CH_2COOH

B CH_3CH_2OH

C $CH_3CH_2COOCH_3$

D $CH_3CH_2CH(CH_3)CH_3$

13 Which two families of compounds react together to produce esters?

A Cycloalkanes and alcohols

B Alkenes and alkanes

C Alkenes and carboxylic acids

D Carboxylic acids and alcohols

14 The half-life of the isotope ^{42}K is 12.4 hours.

What fraction of the original sample will remain after 24.8 hours?

A 0.5

B 0.25

C 0.125

D 0.0625

15 Which of the following diagrams could be used to represent the structure of a metal?

A

B

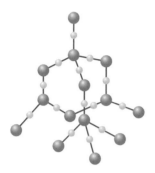

C

D

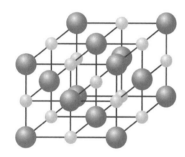

16 Experiments were performed on three metal elements, X, Y and Z, to establish their reactivity.

The results of the experiments are recorded in the table below.

Metal	Reaction with dilute hydrochloric acid	Reaction with water
X	No reaction	No reaction
Y	Fast reaction	Slow reaction
Z	Slow reaction	No reaction

The order of reactivity of the metals, starting with the **least** reactive is

A X, Y, Z

B Y, Z, X

C X, Z, Y

D Y, X, Z.

17 The structure of propene is shown below.

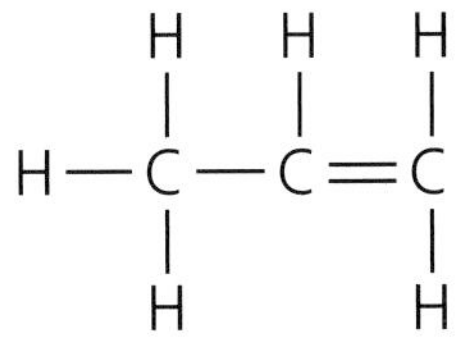

Which of the following is the correct structure of polypropene?

A

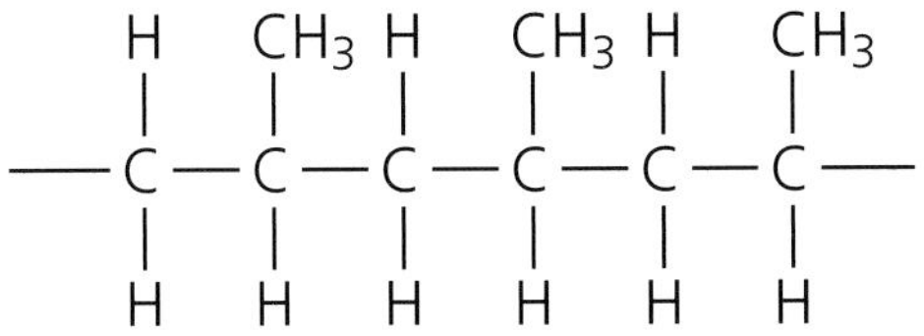

B

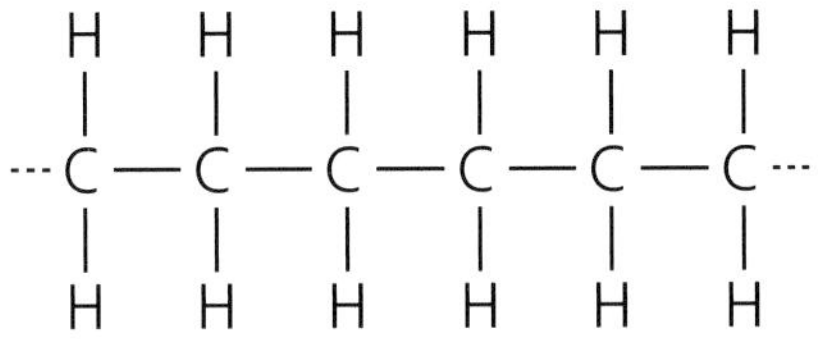

C

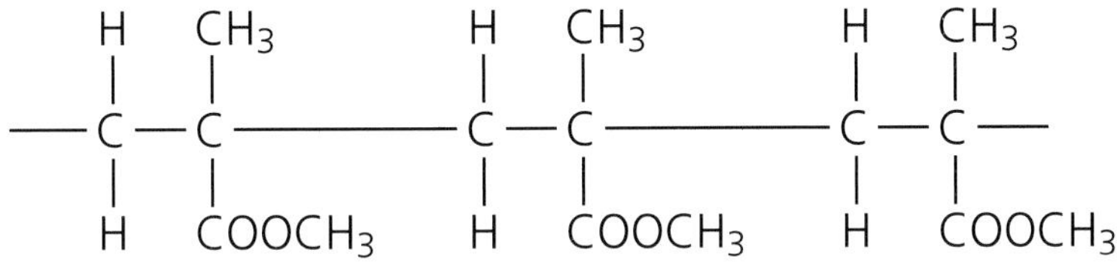

D

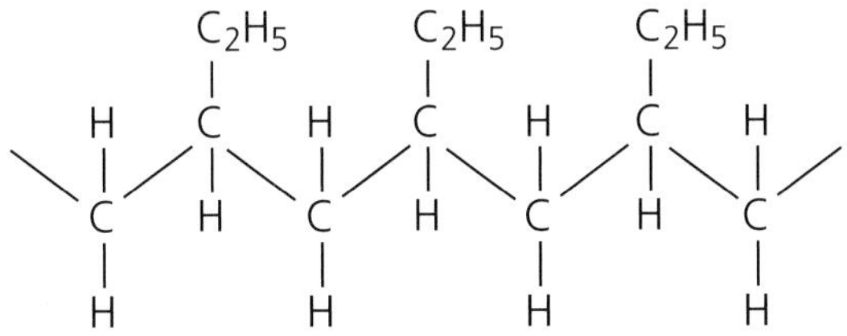

Questions 18 and 19 refer to the equation below.

Copper can be extracted from copper sulfate solution as shown in the equation.

$$CuSO_4(aq) + Mg(s) \rightarrow MgSO_4(aq) + Cu(s)$$

18 Identify the reducing agent in this reaction.

    A Copper

    B Magnesium

    C Sulfate ions

    D Magnesium sulfate

19 Which method could be used to separate the copper from the magnesium sulfate solution?

    A Evaporation

    B Filtration

    C Titration

    D Condensation

20 Which of the following compounds would burn with a red flame?

    A   Barium chloride

    B   Copper chloride

    C   Potassium chloride

    D   Strontium chloride

[End of Section 1]

Section 2

Total marks: 60

Attempt ALL questions.

Write your answers clearly in the spaces provided in this paper. Additional space for answers and rough work is provided at the end of this paper. If you use this space you must clearly identify the question number you are attempting. Any rough work must be written in this space. You should score through your rough work when you have written your final copy.

MARKS

1   The world's supply of titanium metal is produced from titanium tetrachloride. The titanium tetrachloride is reacted with magnesium metal in a procedure known as the Kroll process.

$$2Mg(s) + TiCl_4(l) \rightarrow 2MgCl_2(l) + Ti(s)$$

a)   (i)   Name the type of reaction taking place in the Kroll process.   1

(ii)   Name the reducing agent in the Kroll process.   1

b)   (i)   Titanium tetrachloride is a liquid at room temperature and does not conduct electricity.

What type of bonding does this suggest is present in titanium tetrachloride?   1

(ii)   Draw a diagram to show the shape of a titanium tetrachloride molecule.   1

c)   Calculate the mass, in grams, of titanium produced from 500 g of titanium tetrachloride.

Show your working clearly.   3

2   Acetic acid, which is more commonly known as vinegar, is one of the many carboxylic acids that play an important role in coffee quality.

The properties of acetic acid are shown below.

ACETIC ACID	
Formula	$C_2H_4O_2$
Molecular weight	60.05 g/mol
Melting point	16 °C
Boiling point	117.9 °C
Density	1.05 g/cm³
IUPAC ID	Ethanoic acid

MARKS

a) (i)   Draw the full structural formula of acetic acid.   1

(ii) Name the functional group present in acetic acid.   1

b) Solutions of acetic acid can be used to remove limescale, a build-up of insoluble carbonates, from plumbing fixtures.

(i)   To form a solution, the acetic acid is dissolved in water.
Explain why acetic acid is soluble in water.   1

(ii) What type of reaction occurs between the acetic acid and the limescale?   1

3 Read the passage below and answer the questions which follow.

Philae poses comet chemistry conundrum

As the Philae lander bounced across comet 67P in November 2014, two chemical instruments were able to take tentative 'sniffs' of its environment.

'The Philae data are amazing,' enthuses one scientist, who's studied how comets may have supplied Earth with molecules needed for life. 'These are the first measurements of organic compounds collected directly on a comet or asteroid.'

The best 'sniff' happened automatically 25 minutes after Philae's first contact, while the lander was around 150 metres above the surface. The two instruments, a gas chromatograph and a mass spectrometer, analysed the organic compounds in samples of material from the comet's surface. Sixteen organic compounds were detected, half of which contained nitrogen. These compounds included methylamine (CH_3NH_2), ethanal (CH_3CHO) and 1,2-ethanediol ($CH_2OH)_2$.

MARKS

a) Name the two instruments that were used to detect the organic compounds on the comet.

1

b) How many of the organic compounds found contained nitrogen?

1

c) Ethanal (CH_3CHO) and 1,2-ethanediol are isomers.

   (i) State what is meant by the term isomer.

1

   (ii) Draw a possible structure of ethanal.

1

4   A student has to identify the type of bonding present in an unknown compound.

Using your knowledge of chemistry, suggest how the type of bonding in the compound could be identified.

3

5 The volume of oxygen gas produced when hydrogen peroxide decomposes in the presence of a catalyst was measured and the results plotted onto the graph shown.

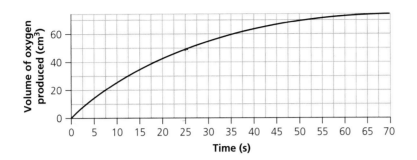

a) Calculate the average rate of reaction, in $cm^3 s^{-1}$, for the first 25 seconds of the reaction.

Show your working clearly.

b) The rate of the reaction slowed as the reaction proceeded.
Suggest a reason for this.

c) Complete the diagram to show how the oxygen gas produced in the reaction may have been collected.

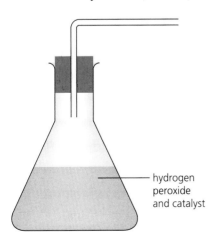

hydrogen peroxide and catalyst

B

6   The energy released by burning methanol can be measured using
     the equipment shown.

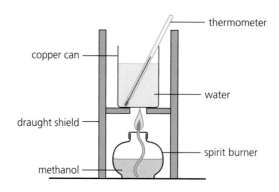

a) (i)   Draw the full structural formula of methanol.   1

    (ii) Name the functional group in methanol.   1

b) What measurements would have to be made to calculate the energy
    released by the alcohol?   1

c) It was found that burning 0.5 g of methanol produced 14 kJ of energy.
    Calculate the energy released, in kJ, when 20 g of methanol is burned.
    Show your working clearly.   2

d) What name is given to reactions that release heat?   1

7 The reactivity series lists metals in order of reactivity.

Using your knowledge of chemistry, suggest how the reactivity of metals can be compared experimentally.

3

8   Biopolymers are natural polymers. An example of a biopolymer is shown below.

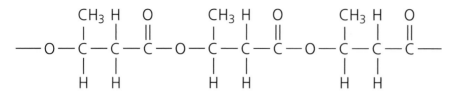

MARKS

a) This polymer is classed as a polyester.

Highlight an ester functional group in the structure of the biopolymer shown above.

1

b) Draw the repeating unit for the biopolymer shown.

1

c) Name the type of polymerisation that takes place to form this biopolymer.

1

9 The first stage of the corrosion of iron involves iron atoms losing electrons to form iron(II) ions.

$$Fe \rightarrow Fe^{2+} + 2e^-$$

a) State the term given to reactions in which electrons are lost.

1

Water and oxygen molecules gain the electrons lost by the iron.

$$2H_2O + O_2 + 4e^- \rightarrow 4OH^-$$

b) Write the redox equation for the overall reaction between the iron, water and oxygen.

1

c) The second stage involves the formation of iron(III) oxide.
    (i) Write the ionic formula of iron(III) oxide.

1

    (ii) State why ionic compounds such as iron(III) oxide conduct electricity when molten.

1

10 Radium was used in the early 1900s to make clock faces and dials glow in the dark. These clocks were made before the effect of radiation was fully understood.

The most common isotope of radium is radium-226, which has a half-life of 1600 years.

MARKS

a) The equation for the decay of radium-226 is

$$^{226}_{88}\text{Ra} \rightarrow \textbf{X} + {}^{4}_{2}\text{He}$$

Name element **X**.

1

b) Name the type of radiation emitted by the radium-226 isotope.

1

c) Another isotope of radium, radium-228, has a half-life of 6 years.
  (i) A sample of radium-228 has a mass of 10 g.
      Calculate the mass of radium-228 that would remain after 18 years.
      Your answer must include the appropriate unit.
      Show your working clearly.

3

  (ii) Suggest why products made in the early 1900s containing radium-226 would still pose a health risk today.

1

11 Ammonium nitrate is a very important fertiliser because it does not break down easily, but due to its explosive nature it must be stored very carefully.

a) Ammonium nitrate provides the element nitrogen which is essential for healthy plant growth.

Name the other two elements that are essential for healthy plant growth.

1

b) Ammonium nitrate is produced by reacting ammonia with nitric acid in a neutralisation reaction.

$$NH_3(l) + HNO_3(aq) \rightarrow NH_4NO_3(aq) + H_2O(l)$$

(i) Name the industrial process used to make ammonia.

1

(ii) Name the spectator ion in this neutralisation reaction.

1

c) Ammonium nitrate is often combined with urea, $CO(NH_2)_2$, for use as a fertiliser.

Calculate the percentage, by mass, of nitrogen in urea.

Show your working clearly.

3

12 Butanoic acid can be used to produce esters, which are used to flavour some foods. The table below gives information on some esters produced using butanoic acid.

Ester	Formula	Boiling point/°C	Flavour / scent
Methylbutanoate	$CH_3CH_2CH_2COOCH_3$	102	Apple
Ethylbutanoate	$CH_3CH_2CH_2COOCH_2CH_3$	121	Pineapple
Propylbutanoate	$CH_3CH_2CH_2COOCH_2CH_2CH_3$	143	Apricot
Butylbutanoate	$CH_3CH_2CH_2COOCH_2CH_2CH_2CH_3$	166	Banana

a) State another use of esters.

1

b) (i) Using the information in the table, make a general statement linking the number of carbon atoms to the boiling point of esters.

1

   (ii) Predict the boiling point of the ester pentylbutanoate.

1

c) State the name of the carboxylic acid that is an isomer of methylbutanoate.

1

13 Superacids are substances with an acidity that is 100 times greater than that of sulfuric acid. The strongest superacid is fluoroantimonic acid.

The pH of fluoroantimonic acid is below zero.

a) For each statement below, circle the correct word from the pair in brackets to complete the sentence.

1

pH is a measure of $\left(\dfrac{\text{hydrogen}}{\text{hydroxide}}\right)$ ions.

Acids contain more $\left(\dfrac{\text{hydrogen}}{\text{hydroxide}}\right)$ ions than water.

b) Fluoroantimonic acid is produced by reacting hydrogen fluoride (HF) with antimony pentafluoride (SbF_5).

$$SbF_5 + HF \rightarrow SbF_6 + H_2F$$

(i) Balance the equation shown.

1

(ii) Draw a diagram, showing all the outer electrons, to represent a molecule of hydrogen fluoride.

1

(iii) If a company can supply antimony pentafluoride for £10 per gram, calculate the cost, in pounds, of one mole of antimony pentafluoride.

3

[End of Section 2]

[END OF PRACTICE PAPER B]

ADDITIONAL SPACE FOR ANSWERS AND ROUGH WORK

National 5 Chemistry

Section 1

Total marks: 20

Attempt ALL questions. Answer grid available at www.hoddereducation.co.uk/updatesandextras.

1   Which of the following elements has similar chemical properties to bromine?

   A   Argon

   B   Calcium

   C   Iodine

   D   Oxygen

Questions 2 and 3 refer to the table shown below.

Particle	Number of protons	Number of electrons	Number of neutrons
W	3	2	3
X	6	6	6
Y	8	8	8
Z	6	6	7

2   Which particle is an ion?

   A   W

   B   X

   C   Y

   D   Z

3   Which pair of particles are isotopes?

   A   W and Y

   B   X and Y

   C   W and Z

   D   X and Z

4   In a chemical reaction, $30 \, cm^3$ of gas was collected in the first 25 seconds.

   What was the average rate of reaction, in $cm^3 \, s^{-1}$, for the first 25 seconds?

   A $\dfrac{25}{30}$

   B $\dfrac{30}{25}$

   C $\dfrac{5}{25}$

   D $\dfrac{25}{5}$

5 What is the charge on the tin ion in $Sn(NO_3)_4$?

    A 3+

    B 3–

    C 4+

    D 4–

6 A solution with a pH lower than seven contains

    A only hydrogen ions

    B more hydrogen ions than hydroxide ions

    C more hydroxide ions than hydrogen ions

    D equal numbers of hydrogen ions and hydroxide ions.

7 Which of the following oxides, when mixed with water, would produce an alkaline solution?

    A Sodium oxide

    B Copper oxide

    C Sulfur dioxide

    D Aluminium oxide

8 $2Na^+(aq) + 2OH^-(aq) + 2H^+(aq) + SO_4^{2-}(aq) \rightarrow 2Na^+(aq) + SO_4^{2-}(aq) + 2H_2O(l)$

The spectator ions in this reaction are

    A $Na^+(aq)$ and $OH^-(aq)$

    B $H^+(aq)$ and $SO_4^{2-}(aq)$

    C $OH^-(aq)$ and $H^+(aq)$

    D $Na^+(aq)$ and $SO_4^{2-}(aq)$.

9

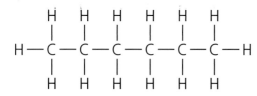

Which of the following is **not** an isomer of the molecule shown?

    A 2-methylpentane

    B 2-methylhexane

    C 3-methylpentane

    D 2,3-dimethylbutane

10 Three members of the ketones homologous series are shown.

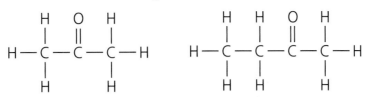

Which of the following is the general formula for the ketones?

A $C_nH_{2n}OH$

B $C_nH_{2n}O$

C $C_nH_{2n+1}O$

D $C_nH_{2n-1}O$

11 Which of the following is **not** the first member of a homologous series?

A Ethene

B Ethanol

C Cyclopropane

D Methanoic acid

12 Which of the following hydrocarbons would decolourise bromine solution quickly?

A $CH_3CH(CH_3)CH_2CH_3$

B $CH_3CH_2CH_2CH_2CH_3$

C $CH_2CHCH_2CH_2CH_3$

D $CH_3CH_2CH_2CH_3$

13 The balanced equation for the complete combustion of hydrocarbon X is shown.

$$X + 5O_2 \rightarrow 3CO_2 + 4H_2O$$

Which of the following is the correct formula of hydrocarbon X?

A C_2H_6

B C_3H_8

C C_3H_6

D C_5H_{12}

14 A reaction is exothermic if

    A   heat energy is taken in during the reaction

    B   the temperature decreases during the reaction

    C   the temperature increases during the reaction

    D   there is no change in temperature during a reaction.

15 Which of the following metals would react with dilute sulfuric acid?

    A   Copper

    B   Silver

    C   Mercury

    D   Lead

16 Which of the following metals can displace iron from a solution of iron(II) sulfate but cannot displace aluminium from a solution of aluminium sulfate?

    A   Nickel

    B   Magnesium

    C   Tin

    D   Zinc

17

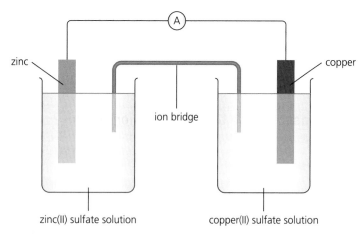

In the cell shown, electrons flow through

    A   the wire from zinc to copper

    B   the wire from copper to zinc

    C   the solution from zinc to copper

    D   the solution from copper to zinc.

18 The structure below shows a section of an addition polymer.

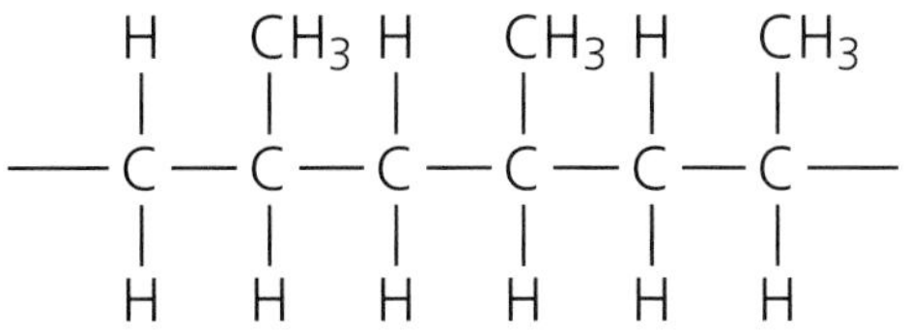

$$\begin{array}{ccccccc} & H & CH_3 & H & CH_3 & H & CH_3 \\ & | & | & | & | & | & | \\ -C & -C & -C & -C & -C & -C- \\ & | & | & | & | & | & | \\ & H & H & H & H & H & H \end{array}$$

Which of the following molecules is used to make this polymer?

A

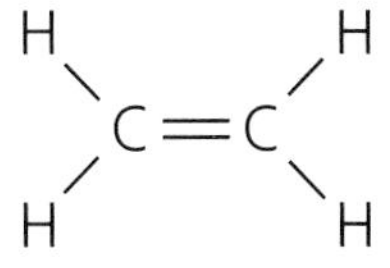

$$\begin{array}{c} H \\ \diagdown \\ H \diagup \end{array} C = C \begin{array}{c} H \\ \diagup \\ \diagdown H \end{array}$$

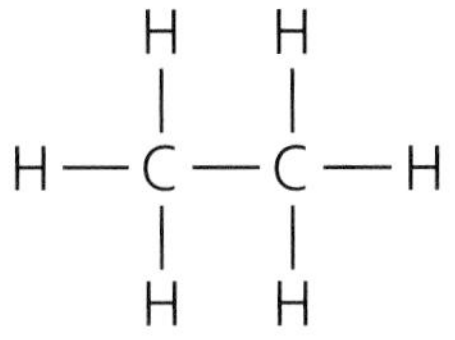

B

$$\begin{array}{cc} H & H \\ | & | \\ H-C-C-H \\ | & | \\ H & H \end{array}$$

C

$$\begin{array}{ccc} H & H & H \\ | & | & | \\ H-C-C-C-H \\ | & | & | \\ H & H & H \end{array}$$

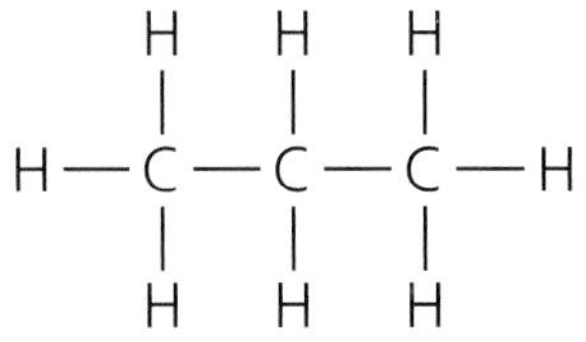

D

$$\begin{array}{c} H \\ \diagdown \\ H \diagup \end{array} C = C \begin{array}{c} CH_3 \\ \diagup \\ \diagdown H \end{array}$$

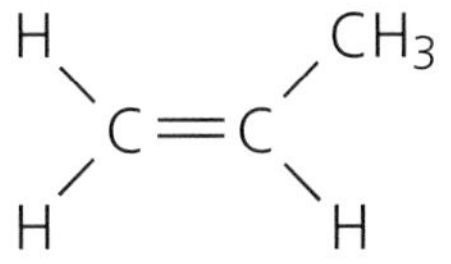

19 Which of the following compounds is used as a starting material in the commercial production of nitric acid?

A Hydrogen fluoride

B Carbon dioxide

C Ammonia

D Methane

20 The graph shows the decay of a radioactive isotope.

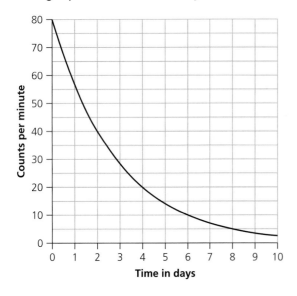

What is the half-life of this isotope?

A 1 day

B 2 days

C 4 days

D 10 days

[End of Section 1]

Section 2

Total marks: 60

Attempt ALL questions.

Write your answers clearly in the spaces provided in this paper. Additional space for answers and rough work is provided at the end of this paper. If you use this space you must clearly identify the question number you are attempting. Any rough work must be written in this space. You should score through your rough work when you have written your final copy.

MARKS

1 Bromine has two stable isotopes, ^{79}Br and ^{81}Br, and over 30 radioisotopes which are unstable.

   a) **(i)** State what is meant by the term isotope.   1

       (ii) The relative atomic mass of bromine is 80.

           What does this suggest about the relative abundance of these isotopes?   1

   b) The nuclide notation of a bromine ion is $^{80}_{35}$Br$^-$.

       Use the nuclide notation to complete the table below for this ion.   2

Particle	Number of each particle
Protons	
Electrons	
Neutrons	

   c) One of the radioisotopes of bromine, bromine-83, has a relative atomic mass of 83 g and a half-life of 2 hours.

       A sample of bromine-83 has a mass of 100 g.

       Calculate the mass, in grams, of bromine-83 that would remain after 8 hours.   2

2 Read the passage below and then answer the questions which follow.

The chemistry of fireworks

The most important component of a firework is, of course, the gunpowder. It was discovered by chance by Chinese alchemists who found that a combination of honey, sulfur and saltpetre (potassium nitrate) would suddenly erupt into flames upon heating.

The combination of sulfur and potassium nitrate was later joined by charcoal in the place of honey – the sulfur and charcoal act as fuels in the reaction, whilst the potassium nitrate works as an oxidising agent, which is necessary to produce the oxygen required to burn the mixture.

Variation in pellet size of the gunpowder and the amount of moisture can be used to significantly increase the burning time for the purposes of fireworks.

The 'stars' contained within the rocket body contain the metal powders or salts that give the firework its colour. Some colours are notoriously hard to produce. The copper-containing compounds tend to be unstable at higher temperatures, and if it reaches these temperatures, it breaks apart, preventing the blue colouration from being exhibited. Purple is also quite hard to produce, as it involves the use of blue-causing compounds in combination with red-causing ones.

MARKS

a) Write the ionic formula of saltpetre.

1

b) What is the purpose of the oxidising agent?

1

c) State the name of a metal that may be added to fireworks to provide a red colour.

1

d) Which two factors affect the rate at which the gunpowder pellets burn?

1

3 A student studying chemistry has discovered a jar in the chemistry storeroom which is known to house a carbon-containing compound, but which has no label attached to it.

Using your knowledge of chemistry, suggest how the student could identify the carbon-containing compound.

4   In 2011 global production of ammonia (NH_3) was over 140 million tonnes
    and production is increasing each year.

   a)   Name the industrial process used to produce ammonia.   1

   b)   Draw a diagram showing how the outer electrons are arranged in
        a molecule of ammonia.   1

   c)   The table below shows the impact that pressure has on the production
        of ammonia at 300 °C.

Pressure/atm	Percentage of ammonia produced/%
25	27
50	40
100	53
200	67
400	80
800	

(i) Draw a line graph of the results.
Use appropriate scales to fit most of the paper.

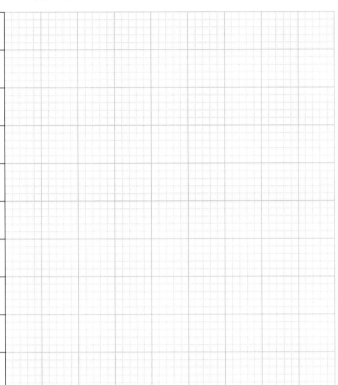

(ii) Predict the percentage of ammonia that would be produced at
800 atmospheres (atm).

d) Ammonium phosphate, $(NH_4)_3PO_4$, is an important fertiliser that can
be produced from ammonia.

(i) Name the essential element required for healthy plant growth that
is **not** supplied by ammonium phosphate fertiliser.

(ii) Calculate the percentage by mass of nitrogen in ammonium phosphate.
Show your working clearly.

5 Many chemical reactions involve the transfer of electrons between two different substances.

Using your knowledge of chemistry, comment on reactions that involve a transfer of electrons.

6 Plutonium-238 is an alpha-emitting radioisotope with a half-life of 90 years.
It can be used to power heart pacemakers for use in the human body. The
pacemaker is contained within a titanium case.

a) The equation for the decay
of plutonium-238 is

$$^{238}_{94}\text{Pu} \rightarrow \textbf{X} + ^{4}_{2}\text{He}$$

(i) Identify element **X**.

1

(ii) Suggest why the alpha radiation emitted poses no health risk
to the patient.

1

b) Some of the pacemakers powered by this radioisotope work for over
25 years before needing to be replaced.

The mass of plutonium-238 remaining in the pacemaker after a period
of time can be calculated using the following equation:

$$\text{mass remaining} = \text{time in use} \times \frac{\text{original mass}}{\text{half-life}}$$

If 0.8 g of plutonium-238 was added to the pacemaker when new, calculate
the mass, in grams, of plutonium-238 that would remain after 25 years.

Show your working clearly.

2

7 Triglycerides are the main constituent of fats and oils. A typical triglyceride is shown.

MARKS

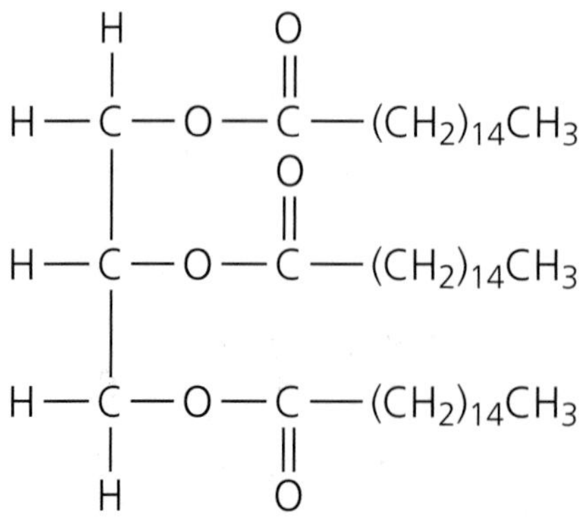

a) To which family of compounds do triglycerides belong?

1

b) Triglycerides are produced by the reaction of a long-chain carboxylic acid and the alcohol glycerol.

(i) Name the functional group present in glycerol.

1

(ii) Butanoic acid can be reacted with glycerol to produce a triglyceride. Draw the full structural formula of butanoic acid.

1

c) Oils have a lower melting point than fats because they are unsaturated. Describe the chemical test, including the result, to show that oils are unsaturated.

1

8 Extraction of magnesium from seawater provides around 60% of the world's supply of magnesium metal.

One method of extracting the magnesium metal from seawater is shown in the flow diagram.

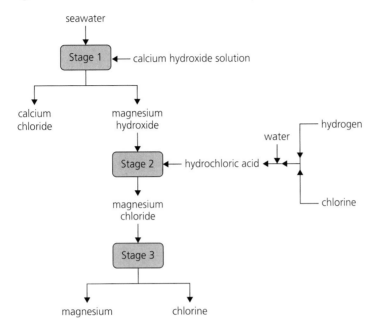

a) What name is given to the reaction taking place in Stage 2?

1

b) In Stage 3, the magnesium chloride solution is separated into magnesium and chlorine by electrolysis.

The ion–electron equations taking place during the electrolysis of magnesium chloride are

$$Mg^{2+} + 2e^- \rightarrow Mg$$
$$Cl^- \rightarrow Cl + e^-$$

(i) Write the redox equation for the overall reaction.

1

(ii) State why ionic compounds such as magnesium chloride can conduct electricity when in solution.

1

c) **On the flow diagram**, draw an arrow to show how the process can be made more economical.

1

C

9   A student was testing the products released on the combustion of ethanol.

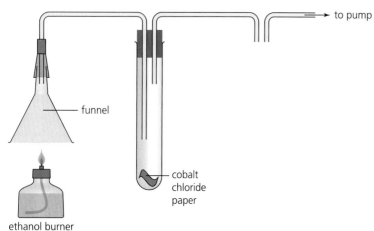

funnel

cobalt
chloride
paper

ethanol burner

to pump

a)   Complete the diagram to show how the student could have tested for
     the production of carbon dioxide.

1

b)   The balanced equation for the combustion of ethanol is

$$C_2H_5OH + 3.5O_2 \rightarrow 2CO_2 + 3H_2O$$

Calculate the mass, in g, of carbon dioxide that is released on
combustion of 4.6 g of ethanol.

Show your working clearly.

3

c)   Energy is also released on combustion of ethanol.
     State the name that is given to reactions that release energy.

1

10 Copper is a very good conductor of both electricity and heat.

a) Explain why metals such as copper can conduct electricity.

1

b) Although copper is a fairly unreactive metal, it will still react with chlorine gas to produce copper(II) chloride.
Write the equation for this reaction. (There is no need to balance the equation.)

1

c) Copper can be extracted from naturally occurring compounds such as malachite.

(i) State the term used to describe naturally occurring metal compounds such as malachite.

1

(ii) During the extraction of copper from its ore, copper ions are converted to copper atoms.
State the name of this type of reaction.

1

11 Vinegar is added to some household cleaning products used to remove limescale on plumbing fixtures.

MARKS

a) Name the type of reaction that takes place between vinegar and the limescale.

1

b) The concentration of ethanoic acid contained in a solution of vinegar can be calculated by titrating a sample with $0.5\,mol\,l^{-1}$ sodium hydroxide solution.

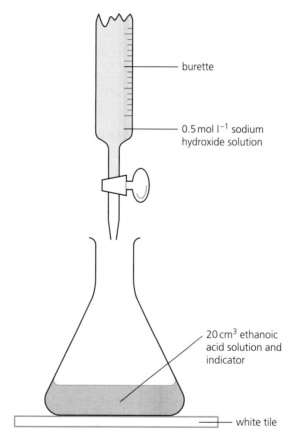

— burette

— $0.5\,mol\,l^{-1}$ sodium hydroxide solution

$20\,cm^3$ ethanoic acid solution and indicator

— white tile

The results of the titration are given in the table.

Titration	Initial burette reading/cm³	Final burette reading/cm³	Titre/cm³
1	0.0	10.5	10.5
2	10.5	20.4	9.9
3	20.4	30.5	10.1

(i) Calculate the average volume, in cm³, of sodium hydroxide used.   1

(ii) The equation for the reaction is

$$NaOH(aq) + CH_3COOH(aq) \rightarrow CH_3COONa(aq) + H_2O \ (l)$$

Calculate the concentration, in mol l⁻¹, of ethanoic acid in the vinegar.
Show your working clearly.   3

12 A solution of hydrogen peroxide can be used to disinfect contact lenses before use. The hydrogen peroxide used must be broken down into oxygen and water before the lenses are used, to avoid damage to the eye.

The equation for this reaction is

$$2H_2O_2 \rightarrow 2H_2O + O_2$$

A student investigated the most effective way to break down the hydrogen peroxide.

MARKS

a) Catalysts increase the rate at which hydrogen peroxide breaks down.

(i) Suggest two other factors that may affect the rate of this reaction.   1

One catalyst that can be used in the lab is manganese dioxide.

(ii) Suggest why the manganese dioxide is more effective when used as a fine powder.   1

b) Using a catalyst, the student collected $15\,cm^3$ of oxygen gas in 45 seconds.

(i) Calculate the average rate of this reaction.
Your answer must include the appropriate unit.
Show your working clearly.   2

(ii) Suggest why the rate of this reaction would decrease as the reaction proceeded.   1

13 Over 60 million tonnes of polyethene is manufactured each year, making it the most common plastic in the world.

    a) Name the type of polymerisation that takes place to form polyethene.

1

    b) (i) Draw the structure of polyethene showing three monomer units combined.

1

    (ii) During the manufacturing process, hydrogen gas is added to the reaction when the polymer chains are at the correct length.

    Suggest why the addition of hydrogen gas stops the production of polyethene.

1

[End of Section 2]

[END OF PRACTICE PAPER C]

ADDITIONAL SPACE FOR ANSWERS AND ROUGH WORK

Additional graph paper for Question 4 c) (i)

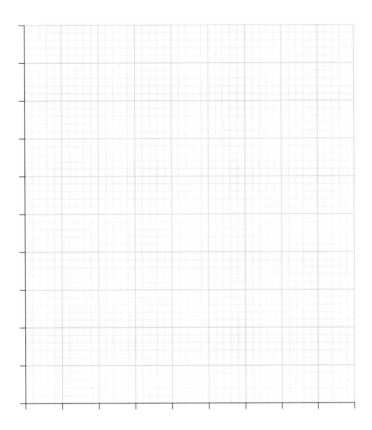

National 5
Chemistry

HODDER
GIBSON
LEARN MORE

Practice Paper A

Section 1

Question	Answer	Hint
1	C	Oxygen exists as a diatomic molecule in which the atoms are held together by covalent bonds. Neon does not form bonds, silicon forms a covalent network and magnesium atoms are held together by metallic bonds.
2	A	The atomic number of an atom is equal to the number of protons, in this case 11; the mass number is equal to the atomic number plus the number of neutrons. In this atom the number of neutrons is equal to 23 – 11 = 12 (mass number – atomic number).
3	D	An ion is a charged particle, which means there is a difference between the number of protons and electrons in the atom. In options A, B and C, the numbers of protons and electrons are equal, which means they are not ions but atoms.
4	D	It is important to learn the shapes of molecules and you should be able to draw and name the shapes. Water is angular, ammonia is (trigonal) pyramidal, carbon dioxide is linear and carbon tetrafluoride is tetrahedral.
5	B	Isotopes have the same atomic number but different mass numbers. Be careful not to get isomers and isotopes confused.
6	C	Titanium ions will carry a positive charge as all metals form positively charged ions. In this case the charge will be 3+ because it is combined to three bromine ions which each carry a –1 charge.
7	A	For a substance to be in the liquid state at 20 °C, the melting point must be below this value and the boiling point must be greater than 20 °C.
8	D	Ionic compounds have high melting points and will conduct electricity only when molten or in solution but not in the solid state because the ions are not free to move.
9	B	At first glance this one seems to be quite tricky. If 0.1 moles is equal to 4.4 g, then 1 mole is equal to 44 g (10 × 4.4). The mass of one mole of carbon dioxide is 44 g.
10	B	**Ionic** substances will conduct electricity when in solution, or when molten, because the **ions** are free to move.
11	C	Soluble metal oxides (bases) dissolve in water to form alkaline solutions, i.e. solutions with a pH greater than 7. Potassium oxide is a soluble oxide but magnesium oxide is insoluble. The table of 'Solubilities of Selected Compounds in Water' is on page 8 of your data booklet.
12	B	To name branched hydrocarbons, identify the longest chain of carbons (butane), then identify the branches (methyl) and number each branch to give the lowest set of numbers (2,2). The 'di' prefix is required to show there are two methyl branches.
13	A	It is important to learn all the homologous series and their functional group. Alcohols contain the hydroxyl functional group (–OH).
14	C	To make this question simpler write down the molecular formula of each diene, e.g. C_3H_4, C_4H_6, C_4H_8. Looking at molecular formulae can make it easier to work out general formulae.

Question	Answer	Hint
15	A	Reduction is the gain of electrons and the zinc(II) ions (Zn^{2+}) are gaining two electrons to form zinc metal.
16	D	The method used to extract a metal from its ore is dependent on the reactivity of the metal. More reactive metals such as aluminium are extracted from their ores by electrolysis.
17	D	The greater the difference in reactivity between the two metals in a cell, the greater the voltage that will be produced by the cell. Aluminium is more reactive than tin, copper and iron and would therefore create the greatest voltage when connected to silver.
18	D	A tricky question. Spectator ions are ions that are unchanged by a chemical reaction; this includes changes in state. The silver and iodide ions change state from aqueous to solid and so they are not spectator ions.
19	B	A precipitation reaction is one in which an insoluble solid is produced by two liquids reacting. The precipitate is silver iodide.
20	A	The monomers for addition polymerisation are unsaturated, which means they contain a carbon-to-carbon double bond. Monomer D would form a different polymer than the one shown.

Section 2

Question			Answer	Hint
1	a)		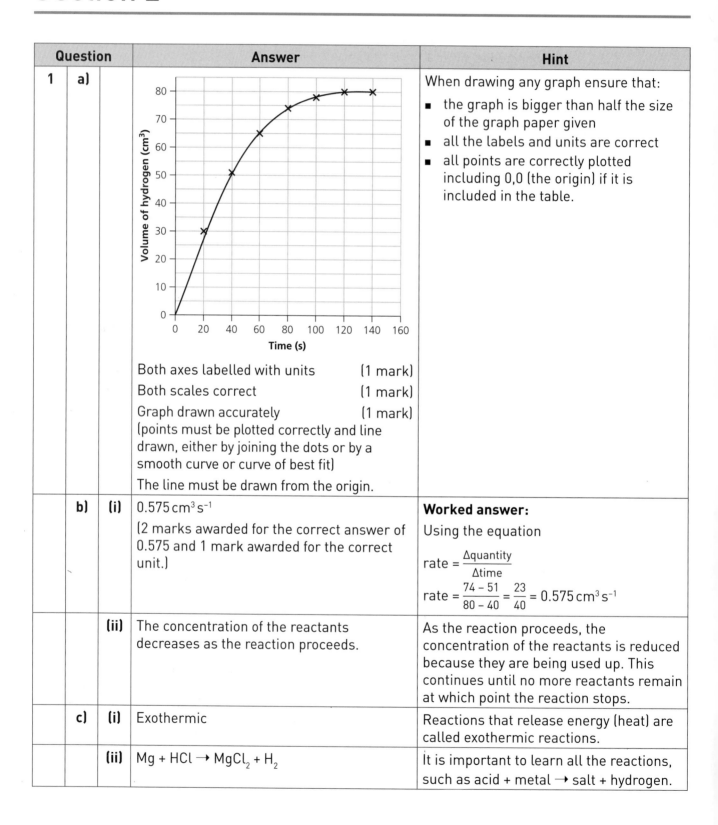 Both axes labelled with units (1 mark) Both scales correct (1 mark) Graph drawn accurately (1 mark) (points must be plotted correctly and line drawn, either by joining the dots or by a smooth curve or curve of best fit) The line must be drawn from the origin.	When drawing any graph ensure that: ■ the graph is bigger than half the size of the graph paper given ■ all the labels and units are correct ■ all points are correctly plotted including 0,0 (the origin) if it is included in the table.
	b)	(i)	$0.575\,cm^3\,s^{-1}$ (2 marks awarded for the correct answer of 0.575 and 1 mark awarded for the correct unit.)	**Worked answer:** Using the equation $rate = \dfrac{\Delta quantity}{\Delta time}$ $rate = \dfrac{74-51}{80-40} = \dfrac{23}{40} = 0.575\,cm^3\,s^{-1}$
		(ii)	The concentration of the reactants decreases as the reaction proceeds.	As the reaction proceeds, the concentration of the reactants is reduced because they are being used up. This continues until no more reactants remain at which point the reaction stops.
	c)	(i)	Exothermic	Reactions that release energy (heat) are called exothermic reactions.
		(ii)	$Mg + HCl \rightarrow MgCl_2 + H_2$	It is important to learn all the reactions, such as acid + metal $\rightarrow$ salt + hydrogen.

Question			Answer	Hint
2			**Open-ended question** 3 marks: The candidate has demonstrated a good conceptual understanding of the chemistry involved. 2 marks: The candidate has demonstrated a reasonable understanding of the chemistry involved. 1 mark: The candidate has demonstrated a limited understanding of the chemistry involved. 0 marks: The candidate has demonstrated no understanding of the chemistry that is relevant to the problem/situation. The candidate has made no statement(s) that is/are relevant to the problem/situation.	Open-ended questions have no single correct answer. Listed below are **some** of the options that may be included and explained in your answer. **This list is not exhaustive and you do not have to include all of these to gain the full 3 marks**. Ensure that what you have included has been explained fully and clearly. Include diagrams, equations, etc. that may help with your explanation. ■ Ionic bonding: ions, positive metal ions, negative non-metal ions, electrostatic attraction. ■ Covalent bonding: positive nuclei, negative shared electrons. ■ Electrolysis: ions, positive metal ions moving to the negative electrode, negative non-metal ions moving to the positive electrode, extraction of metals. ■ Atoms: positive nucleus, protons, electrons, neutrons.
3	a)		To provide the essential nutrients for plant growth.	Fertilisers provide plants with nitrogen, potassium and phosphorus which are essential for healthy plant growth.
	b)		Carbon dioxide, methane and nitrous oxide	Make sure to read the passage carefully as the answer to this question is contained within it: *'After carbon dioxide and methane, nitrous oxide is believed to be the largest factor in climate change ...'*
	c)	(i)	35%	**Worked answer:** Step 1: Calculate the gram formula mass of ammonium nitrate using the formula NH_4NO_3 $(14 \times 1) + (1 \times 4) + (14 \times 1) + (16 \times 3) = 80$ Step 2: Calculate the mass of nitrogen in the compound. Each molecule contains two nitrogen atoms so the mass of nitrogen in the compound is $2 \times 14 = 28$. Step 3: Calculate the percentage by mass using the following equation, which is on page 1 of your data booklet. % by mass $= \dfrac{m}{GFM} \times 100 = \dfrac{28}{80} \times 100 = 35\%$

Question			Answer	Hint
		(ii)	$NH_4^+NO_3^-$	The following answers would also be accepted here: $(NH_4^+)(NO_3^-)$ or $(NH_4^+)NO_3^-$ or $NH_4^+ (NO_3^-)$.
	d)		500 kg	Make sure to read the passage carefully as the answer to this question is contained within it: '… that's the ratio of the amount of nitrogen that's used by the plant to the amount that's applied and that's sometimes around 50% …' So if 1000 kg is applied, 500 kg, i.e. 50% would be used by the plants.
4	a)	(i)	–20 (accept answer between –22 and –18)	The drop in octane number follows a regular pattern according to the values in the table. Establish the pattern and you should calculate the octane number of octane to be –20.
		(ii)	The greater the number of carbon atoms, the less efficient the fuel is.	
	b)		60.61 kJ	**Worked answer:** Using the equation $\Delta H = cm\Delta T$ allows you to calculate the energy released. $c = 4.18$ (value from the data booklet) m = mass of water (not hexane) is $500/1000 = 0.5$ kg ΔT = change in temperature = $49 – 20 = 29$ Putting these values into the equation gives: $\Delta H = cm\Delta T = 4.18 \times 0.5 \times 29 = 60.61$ kJ
	c)	(i)		When drawing structural formulae, make sure that each carbon atom has formed four bonds and that all the hydrogen atoms and bonds are shown.
		(ii)	An isomer has the same molecular formula but a different structural formula.	Be careful not to get isomers and isotopes confused.

	Question		Answer	Hint
5			**Open-ended question** 3 marks: The candidate has demonstrated a good conceptual understanding of the chemistry involved. 2 marks: The candidate has demonstrated a reasonable understanding of the chemistry involved. 1 mark: The candidate has demonstrated a limited understanding of the chemistry involved. 0 marks: The candidate has demonstrated no understanding of the chemistry that is relevant to the problem/situation. The candidate has made no statement(s) that is/are relevant to the problem/situation.	Open-ended questions have no single correct answer. Listed below are **some** of the options that may be included and explained in your answer. **This list is not exhaustive and you do not have to include all of these to gain the full 3 marks**. Ensure that what you have included has been explained fully and clearly. Include diagrams, equations, etc. that may help with your explanation. ■ Titrations: calculations, experiment description, alkali, neutralisation. ■ Neutralisation: base, carbonate, limescale, measure carbon dioxide released, experiment description, rate of reaction. ■ Conductivity: concentration effect on conductivity, H^+ ions. ■ pH testing.
6	a)		Ores	Most metals are found in nature not as a pure metal but as compounds. These compounds are called ores.
	b)	(i)	$Fe^{3+} + 3e^- \rightarrow Fe$	The reduction reaction equations are listed on page 10 of your data booklet.
		(ii)	700 g	**Worked answer:** Step 1: Establish the molar ratio. 1 mole of Fe_2O_3 reacts to produce 2 moles of Fe. Step 2: Calculate the moles of Fe_2O_3 using moles = mass ÷ formula mass ($1000 ÷ 160 = 6.25$). The gram formula mass of Fe_2O_3 is $(2 \times 56) + (3 \times 16) = 160$ g. Step 3: Use the ratio to establish the moles of iron produced ($6.25 \times 2 = 12.5$ moles of iron produced). Step 4: Calculate the mass of iron produced using mass = moles × formula mass ($12.5 \times 56 = 700$ g)
7	a)		Carboxyl functional group	It is important to learn the names and be able to identify all of the functional groups. As part of your revision it is good practice to create a table listing all the homologous series and their functional groups.
	b)		It can form intermolecular attractions with water molecules.	A difficult question. You should be able to explain the melting point, boiling point, and solubility of carboxylic acids in terms of intermolecular bonds (bonds between molecules).

Question			Answer	Hint
	c)	(i)	Alcohol	Alcohols react with carboxylic acids to form esters in a condensation reaction.
		(ii)	Any suitable use such as solvents, perfumes, fragrances, preservatives.	Esters have many uses.
8	a)		15.0 cm³	When calculating the average volume used, it is important to remember *not* to include the 1st or rough titration value. The average for this titration is (15.1 + 14.9)/2 = 15.0
	b)		0.15 mol l⁻¹	**Worked answer:** Step 1: Establish the molar ratio. 1 mole of HCl reacts with 1 mole of NaOH. Step 2: Calculate the number of moles of HCl by using $N = C \times V$ (0.1 × 15/1000 = 0.0015 moles). Step 3: Use the ratio to establish the moles of NaOH reacted and because the ratio is one to one, the number of moles of NaOH reacted is also 0.0015 moles. Step 4: Calculate the concentration of NaOH using $C = N \div V = 0.0015 \div 10/1000 = 0.15 \text{ mol l}^{-1}$
9	a)		Atoms with the same atomic number but a different mass number	Don't get this mixed up with isomers.
	b)		$^{241}_{95}\text{Am} \rightarrow {}^{237}_{93}\text{Np} + {}^{4}_{2}\alpha$ or $^{241}_{95}\text{Am} \rightarrow {}^{237}_{93}\text{Np} + {}^{4}_{2}\text{He}$	Both the symbol for alpha (α) or the symbol of helium (He) can be used but the atomic numbers and mass numbers must be present and correct.
	c)		The time it takes for a radioisotope's activity to fall by half.	
10	a)		Protons = 19 Neutrons = 20	The number of protons contained within an atom is equal to the atomic number. The number of neutrons is equal to the mass number – the atomic number (39 – 19 = 20).
	b)		Atoms gain or lose electrons to achieve a stable electron arrangement like that of a noble gas.	
	c)	(i)		It is good practice to pair the electrons together. Make sure that the electrons are on the line of the energy level. Remember to read questions carefully as the question asks you to complete the electron arrangement of the **ion** and not the **atom**, so the single outer electron of the potassium atom should not be included in the diagram.

Question			Answer	Hint
		(ii)	The (electrostatic) force of attraction between the positive nucleus (protons) and the negative electrons.	
		(iii)	$Mg(g) \rightarrow Mg^+(g) + e^-$	The clue to this answer is in the question. The question shows the first ionisation energy of potassium and all you have to do is rewrite the equation but using the symbol of magnesium (Mg) rather than potassium (K). The state symbols are not required.
11	a)	(i)	Addition polymerisation	The clue is in the structure of the monomer. If the monomer is unsaturated (has a carbon-to-carbon double bond), then it will form a polymer by addition polymerisation.
		(ii)		When drawing a repeating unit, make sure that you draw both 'end' bonds to show that this unit is joining on to other units. Remember also to change the double bond to a single bond.
	b)		Cyanoacrylate would decolourise bromine solution.	An addition reaction would occur between the double bond of the cyanoacrylate and the bromine solution resulting in the bromine solution turning from brown/orange to colourless.
12	a)	(i)	Haber process	It is important to learn both the balanced equation and the catalyst used in the Haber process. Equation: $3H_2 + N_2 \rightarrow 2NH_3$ Catalyst: iron
		(ii)		When drawing diagrams like this, ensure that the bonding electrons are on the line or within the overlapped area. The answer shown demonstrates the variations of the bonding electrons that are accepted. You must also ensure that you have included the symbols of the elements involved.
	b)	(i)	Water (H_2O)	Nitrogen dioxide (NO_2) will dissolve in water to produce nitric acid (HNO_3).

Question			Answer	Hint
		(ii)		An arrow should be drawn from the unreacted nitrogen monoxide (NO) to the nitrogen monoxide above the reactor. The direction of the arrow must also be correct to be awarded the mark.
		(iii)	To allow the process to be performed at lower temperatures. To increase the rate of the reaction. To save energy.	Catalysts are used regularly in industry to allow processes to be done at lower temperatures which saves both money and energy.
	c)	(i)	$2HNO_3(aq) + Ca(OH)_2(aq) \rightarrow Ca(NO_3)_2(aq) + 2H_2O(l)$	Balancing equations is an essential skill for any chemist and most exams will ask you to balance an equation.
		(ii)	Heat the solution to evaporate off the water.	Evaporation is used to separate a soluble solid from solution. The separation techniques of distillation, evaporation, chromatography and filtration are used regularly in the laboratory and as a result will appear regularly in National 5 exam papers.

In the diagram cell: air — NH₃ — purification — heated platinum gauze — NO — air — reactor — X — NO₂ — HNO₃ and unreacted NO.

Practice Paper B

Section 1

Question	Answer	Hint
1	D	To answer this question you must refer to page 7 of your data booklet. Barium, calcium and magnesium were all discovered in 1808 and only potassium was discovered before this date (1807).
2	C	All halogens have seven outer electrons and this is why they are placed in Group 7. It is the number of outer electrons which gives an element its chemical properties.
3	D	Carbon dioxide exists as a diatomic molecule in which the atoms are held together by covalent bonds. Neon does not form bonds, silicon dioxide forms a covalent network and calcium chloride is held together by ionic bonds.
4	C	It is important to learn the shapes of molecules and you should be able to draw and name the shapes.
5	B	Titanium ions will carry a positive charge as all metals form positively charged ions. In this case, the charge will be 2+ because it is combined to one oxygen ion, which carries a 2– charge.
6	A	A base is a soluble metal oxide. Options B and C are both non-metal oxides and option D is a salt of sulfuric acid.
7	C	Balancing equations is an essential skill for any chemist and most chemistry exams will ask you to balance an equation.
8	C	If 0.1 moles is equal to 4.6 g then 1 mole is equal to 46 g (10 × 4.6). The mass of one mole of nitrogen dioxide (NO_2) is 46 g.
9	C	Cycloalkanes have the general formula of C_nH_{2n}. The only option that agrees with this general formula is C_4H_8.
10	B	To name branched hydrocarbons, identify the longest chain of carbons (hexane), identify the branches (methyl) and number each branch to give the lowest set of numbers (2,4). The 'di' prefix is required to show that there are two methyl branches.
11	C	To make this question simpler, write down the molecular formula of each alkyne, e.g. C_2H_2, C_3H_4, C_4H_6. Looking at molecular formulae can make it easier to work out general formulae.
12	B	It is important to learn all the homologous series and their functional groups. Alcohols contain the hydroxyl functional group (–OH).
13	D	Esters are formed by the reaction of a carboxylic acid and an alcohol.
14	B	If the half-life of the isotope is 12.4 hours, then after 24.8 hours the sample would have halved twice.
15	C	It is important to be able to identify types of structures from diagrams. Option A is a covalent molecule, option B is a covalent network and option D is an ionic lattice.
16	C	Metal X does not react with acid or water and so is the least reactive of the three. Metal Z does not react with water but does react slowly with acid. Metal Y reacts with both acid and water and is therefore the more reactive of the three.

Question	Answer	Hint
17	A	This one is a tricky question. The double bonds of the monomers combine during addition polymerisation, so the CH_3 must be moved up to allow the double bonds of the monomers to combine.
18	B	The copper ions are reduced (gain electrons) in this reaction. The magnesium provides the electrons for the copper and is therefore the reducing agent in this reaction.
19	B	Filtration is used to separate an insoluble solid from a liquid and because the copper is solid (insoluble), it can be removed by filtration.
20	D	Page 6 of your data booklet provides the flame colours for several elements.

Practice Paper B

Section 2

Question			Answer	Hint
1	a)	(i)	Redox (displacement)	Precipitation is not accepted here because there are solid substances on both sides of the equation (Mg and Ti).
		(ii)	Magnesium	The magnesium is the reducing agent as it supplies the electrons for the titanium ions.
	b)	(i)	Covalent (molecular)	The properties of a substance give a clear indication of the type of bonding contained within it. Only covalent molecular substances have low melting points and would be liquid or gas at room temperature.
		(ii)		Titanium tetrachloride is tetrahedral in shape. Both the name (titanium tetrafluoride) and the formula ($TiCl_4$) give clear clues to the shape of this molecule.
	c)		126 g	**Worked answer:** Step 1: Establish the molar ratio from the balanced equation. 1 mole of $TiCl_4$ reacts to produce 1 mole of Ti. Step 2: Calculate the moles of $TiCl_4$ using, moles = mass ÷ gram formula mass (500 ÷ 190 = 2.63). (The gram formula mass of $TiCl_4$ is (48) + (4 × 35.5) = 190 g.) Step 3: Use the ratio to establish the moles of titanium produced (2.63 × 1 = 2.63 moles of Ti produced). Step 4: Calculate the mass of titanium produced using, mass = moles × formula mass (2.63 × 48 = 126 g).

Question			Answer	Hint
2	a)	(i)		When drawing the full structural formula of any compound, always ensure that each element has formed the correct number of bonds: ■ carbon – four bonds ■ hydrogen – one bond ■ oxygen – two bonds. You must also ensure that: ■ all bonds are shown ■ all symbols are correct ■ the bond from the 'C' goes to the 'O' of the 'OH' and not the 'H'.
		(ii)	Carboxyl functional group	It is important to learn the names of and be able to identify all of the functional groups. As part of your revision, it is good practice to create a table listing all the homologous series and their functional groups.
	b)	(i)	Carboxylic acids are soluble because they can form intermolecular bonds with water molecules.	This is a tricky question but make sure that you learn the answer to this one.
		(ii)	Neutralisation	Limescale would react with acetic acid in a neutralisation reaction.
3	a)		Gas chromatograph and mass spectrometer	Make sure to read the passage carefully as the answer to this question is contained within it: *'The two instruments, a gas chromatograph and a mass spectrometer, analysed the organic compounds in samples …'*
	b)		8	Make sure to read the passage carefully as the answer to this question is contained within it: *'Sixteen organic compounds were detected, half of which contained nitrogen.'*
	c)	(i)	Compounds with the same molecular formula but different structural formulae.	Be careful not to get the definitions of isomers and isotopes confused.
		(ii)		When drawing the full structural formula of any compound, always ensure that each element has formed the correct number of bonds: ■ carbon – four bonds ■ hydrogen – one bond ■ oxygen – two bonds. You must also ensure that: ■ all bonds are shown ■ all symbols are correct ■ the bond from the 'C' goes to the 'O' of the 'OH' and not the 'H'.

Question			Answer	Hint
4			**Open-ended question** 3 marks: The candidate has demonstrated a good conceptual understanding of the chemistry involved. 2 marks: The candidate has demonstrated a reasonable understanding of the chemistry involved. 1 mark: The candidate has demonstrated a limited understanding of the chemistry involved. 0 marks: The candidate has demonstrated no understanding of the chemistry that is relevant to the problem/situation. The candidate has made no statement(s) that is/are relevant to the problem/situation.	Open-ended questions have no single correct answer. Listed below are **some** of the options that may be included and explained in your answer. **This list is not exhaustive and you do not have to include all of these to gain the full 3 marks.** Ensure that what you have included has been explained fully and clearly. Include diagrams, equations, etc. that may help with your explanation. ■ Ionic: solubility, melting point, conductivity. ■ Covalent: solubility, melting point, conductivity, molecular, network. ■ Metallic: solubility, melting point, conductivity.
5	a)		$2\,cm^3\,s^{-1}$	**Worked answer:** Using the equation $$rate = \frac{\Delta quantity}{\Delta t}$$ $$rate = \frac{50}{25} = 2\,cm^3\,s^{-1}$$
	b)		The concentration of the reactants decreased or the reactants are being used up.	As a reaction proceeds, the concentration of the reactants decreases as they react to form the products. When the reactants are used up, the reaction stops.
	c)		oxygen gas collected / measuring cylinder / hydrogen peroxide and catalyst	The marker should assess these questions by asking, 'Will this experiment work as drawn?' Ensure that your diagram is clearly labelled and is not too small.
6	a)	(i)		When drawing the full structural formula of any compound, always ensure that each element has formed the correct number of bonds: ■ carbon – four bonds ■ hydrogen – one bond ■ oxygen – two bonds. You must also ensure that: ■ all bonds are shown ■ all symbols are correct ■ the bond from the 'C' goes to the 'O' of the 'OH' and not the 'H'.

Question			Answer	Hint
		(ii)	Hydroxyl functional group	
	b)		Mass/volume of water Temperature of the water before and after the experiment took place	
	c)		560 kJ	**Worked answer:** 0.5 g = 14 kJ 20 g = (20 ÷ 0.5) × 14 = 560 If 0.5 g of methanol produced 14 kJ of energy, then 20 g produces 560 kJ.
	d)		Exothermic	All combustion reactions are exothermic.
7			**Open-ended question** 3 marks: The candidate has demonstrated a good conceptual understanding of the chemistry involved. 2 marks: The candidate has demonstrated a reasonable understanding of the chemistry involved. 1 mark: The candidate has demonstrated a limited understanding of the chemistry involved. 0 marks: The candidate has demonstrated no understanding of the chemistry that is relevant to the problem/situation. The candidate has made no statement(s) that is/are relevant to the problem/situation.	Open-ended questions have no single correct answer. Listed below are **some** of the options that may be included and explained in your answer. **This list is not exhaustive and you do not have to include all of these to gain the full 3 marks.** Ensure that what you have included has been explained fully and clearly. Include diagrams, equations, etc. that may help with your explanation. ■ Reactions with acids: description of how to perform the experiment, recorded results could include, mass loss due to gas given off, collection of gas produced, observation of rate of bubbles being produced, how to use results/observations. ■ Reactions with oxygen, water and acids: although this would not allow you to differentiate (tell the difference) between metals such as copper and gold. ■ Extraction from ores: methods used to extract metals from their ores. ■ Cells: voltage, electrolyte, explanation of results.
8	a)			Esters can be identified by their functional group –COO–.
	b)			When drawing repeating units, always ensure that you include the end bonds.
	c)		Condensation polymerisation	All polyesters are condensation polymers.
9	a)		Oxidation	Oxidation reactions involve the loss of electrons and reduction reactions involve the gain of electrons. In this example the iron is losing two electrons to form iron(II) ions.

Question			Answer	Hint
	b)		$2Fe + 2H_2O + O_2 \rightarrow 2Fe^{2+} + 4OH^-$	To combine the two equations correctly, they must have equal amounts of electrons. In order to achieve this, the equation containing iron must be multiplied by two so that both equations have four electrons.
	c)	(i)	$(Fe^{3+})_2(O^{2-})_3$	$Fe^{3+}_2 O^{2-}_3$ and $2Fe^{3+} 3O^{2-}$ would also be accepted.
		(ii)	Ions are free to move	When ionic compounds are molten or in solution, they are able to conduct because the ions are free to move (not electrons).
10	a)		Radon or Rn	$^{222}_{86}Rn$ would also be accepted but the atomic and mass numbers must be correct. The numbers on both sides of the equation must balance.
	b)		Alpha	Alpha radiation can be represented as a He particle with the mass of 4.
	c)	(i)	1.25 g (2 marks for 1.25 and 1 mark for the correct unit (g).)	The half-life of the isotope is 6 years so in 18 years it would have halved three times (0 – 6 – 12 – 18). This means that the mass would have halved three times (10 – 5 – 2.5 – 1.25). The correct unit must also be included in this answer to gain the additional mark.
		(ii)	It would still be radioactive due to its long half-life.	Radium-226 has a half-life of 1600 years and so would still be very radioactive today.
11	a)		Phosphorus and potassium	Phosphorus, potassium and nitrogen are essential nutrients for healthy plant growth.
	b)	(i)	Haber process	It is important to learn both the balanced equation and the catalyst used in the Haber process: equation: $3H_2 + N_2 \rightarrow 2NH_3$ catalyst: iron.
		(ii)	NO_3^- or nitrate ion	A spectator ion passes through a reaction unchanged.
	c)		47%	**Worked answer:** Step 1: Calculate the gram formula mass of urea using the formula $CO(NH_2)_2$. $(12 \times 1) + (16 \times 1) + (14 \times 2) + (1 \times 2 \times 2) = 60$ Step 2: Calculate the mass of nitrogen in the compound. Each molecule contains two nitrogen atoms so the mass of nitrogen in the compound is $2 \times 14 = 28$. Step 3: Calculate the percentage by mass using the following equation, which is on page 1 of your data booklet: % by mass $= \dfrac{m}{GFM} \times 100 = \dfrac{28 \times 100}{60} = 47\%$
12	a)		Any suitable use such as solvents, perfumes, fragrances, preservatives.	Esters have many uses.

Question			Answer	Hint
	b)	(i)	The more carbons an ester contains, the higher the boiling point is.	The information required to answer these questions is normally provided in a table form. Spend some time looking at all the information provided and make a summary of it.
		(ii)	190 °C	The table again provides the information required to predict the boiling point of pentylbutanoate. Look at the regular increase in boiling point between the esters: methyl to ethyl – increase of 19 °C, ethyl to propyl – increase of 22 °C, propyl to butyl – increase of 23 °C.
				So an increase of approximately 24 would be expected.
				In a predicting question there is always a range in which your answer must fall to be awarded the mark; in this case 189–193 would be acceptable.
	c)		Pentanoic acid	Methylbutanoate has five carbon atoms and so the carboxylic acid with five carbons atoms must be the isomer.
13	a)		Hydrogen/hydrogen	pH (potential Hydrogen) is a measure of the hydrogen ion concentration and all acidic solutions contain more hydrogen ions than hydroxide ions.
	b)	(i)	$SbF_5 + 2HF \rightarrow SbF_6 + H_2F$	Balancing equations is an essential skill for any chemist and most exams will ask you to balance an equation.
		(ii)		When drawing diagrams like this, ensure that the bonding electrons are on the line or within the overlapped area.
				You must also ensure that you have included the symbols of the elements involved.
		(iii)	£2170	**Worked answer:**
				Step 1: Calculate the gram formula mass of antimony pentafluoride using the formula SbF_5, $(122 \times 1) + (19 \times 5) = 217\,g$.
				Step 2: Multiply the gram formula mass by 10 as each gram costs £10.
				$10 \times 217 = £2170$

Practice Paper C

Section 1

Question	Answer	Hint
1	C	Elements in the same group of the Periodic Table have similar chemical properties because they have the same number of outer electrons.
2	A	An ion is a charged particle, which means there is a difference between the number of protons and electrons. In options B, C and D, the numbers of protons and electrons are equal, which means they are not ions but atoms.
3	D	Isotopes have the same atomic number but a different number of neutrons. Be careful not to get isomers and isotopes confused.
4	B	Rate is equal to change in quantity divided by the change in time.
5	C	Tin ions will carry a positive charge as all metals form positively charged ions. In this case the charge will be 4+ because it is combined to four nitrate ions which each carry a 1– charge.
6	B	An acidic solution has a greater concentration of H^+ ions than OH^- ions.
7	A	Soluble metal oxides (bases) dissolve in water to form alkaline solutions, i.e. solutions with a pH greater than 7. Sodium oxide is a soluble oxide but copper oxide and aluminium oxide are insoluble. The table of 'Solubilities of Selected Compounds in Water' is on page 8 of your data booklet.
8	D	Spectator ions are ions that are unchanged by a chemical reaction; this includes changes in state. The sodium and sulfate ions are unchanged by this reaction.
9	B	The molecule shown (hexane) has six carbon atoms. Option B (2-methylhexane) has seven carbons atoms and as a result cannot be an isomer of hexane.
10	B	To make this question simpler, write down the molecular formula of each ketone, e.g. C_3H_6O, C_4H_8O, $C_5H_{10}O$. Looking at molecular formulae can make it easier to work out a general formula.
11	B	Methanol is an alcohol and so would be the first member of the alcohol homologous series, making ethanol the second member.
12	C	Molecule C is unsaturated, i.e. contains a carbon-to-carbon double bond, and so would decolourise bromine solution. Drawing out the full structural formula of each option makes this type of question much easier to answer.
13	B	The balanced equation allows you to work out the formula of hydrocarbon X; $3CO_2$ means that the hydrocarbon must have three carbon atoms and the $4H_2O$ means that it must have eight hydrogen atoms: C_3H_8.
14	C	Exothermic reactions release heat energy; for example, combustion is an exothermic reaction.
15	D	Lead is above hydrogen in the electrochemical series and would therefore react with an acid.
16	D	Only a metal that is more reactive than iron can displace it from solution.
17	A	In a cell the electrons travel from the most reactive metal to the least reactive metal along the wires and not through the solution.

Question	Answer	Hint
18	D	The monomers for addition polymerisation are unsaturated, which means they contain a carbon-to-carbon double bond.
19	C	Ammonia from the Haber process is used to manufacture nitric acid.
20	B	Half-life is the time taken for the activity of a radioisotope to fall by half. The activity of this radioisotope starts at 80 counts per minute and takes two days to drop to 40 counts per minute.

Practice Paper C

Section 2

Question			Answer	Hint
1	a)	(i)	Same atomic number but different mass number	Isotopes have identical numbers of protons (atomic number) but they have different numbers of neutrons which results in them having a different mass number.
		(ii)	Equal abundance of each isotope	The relative atomic mass (RAM) will be closest to the most abundant isotope. In this case, the RAM is exactly half way between the two isotopes and this indicates that there are equal amounts of each isotope.
	b)		Protons = 35 Electrons = 36 Neutrons = 45	The particle shown is an ion which means that there is a difference in the number of protons and electrons. In this case the ion is negatively charged and so has one more electron than proton. The number of neutrons is equal to the mass number minus the atomic number (80 – 35 = 45).
	c)		6.25 g	After 8 hours the isotope would have halved four times (8/2 = 4). If you halve the mass four times, you will arrive at the correct answer (100 – 50 – 25 – 12.5 – 6.25).
2	a)		$K^+NO_3^-$	The following answers would also be accepted here: $(K^+)(NO_3^-), (K^+)NO_3^-$ or $K^+(NO_3^-)$.
	b)		To provide the oxygen for combustion	Make sure to read the passage carefully as the answer to this question is contained within it: *'... the potassium nitrate works as an oxidising agent, which is necessary to produce the oxygen required to burn the mixture.'*

Question			Answer	Hint
	c)		Calcium, strontium or lithium	The flame colours of selected elements are on page 6 of your data booklet.
	d)		Pellet size and moisture	Make sure to read the passage carefully as the answer to this question is contained within it: *'Variation in pellet size of the gunpowder and the amount of moisture can be used to significantly increase the burning time for …'*
3			**Open-ended question** 3 marks: The candidate has demonstrated a good conceptual understanding of the chemistry involved. 2 marks: The candidate has demonstrated a reasonable understanding of the chemistry involved. 1 mark: The candidate has demonstrated a limited understanding of the chemistry involved. 0 marks: The candidate has demonstrated no understanding of the chemistry that is relevant to the problem/situation. The candidate has made no statement(s) that is/are relevant to the problem/situation.	Open-ended questions have no single correct answer. Listed below are **some** of the options that may be included and explained in your answer. **This list is not exhaustive and you do not have to include all of these to gain the full 3 marks.** Ensure that what you have included has been explained fully and clearly. Include diagrams, equations, etc. that may help with your explanation. ■ Melting point analysis: data booklet comparison. ■ Solubility tests: explanation of results. ■ Products of combustion: experiment description, observations, explanation of results. ■ Reactions with various substances, e.g. acid to identify carbonates, ester formation (alcohol and carboxylic acid), explanation of results/observations. ■ Bromine test for unsaturation: experiment description, observations, explanation of results.
4	a)		Haber process	It is important to learn both the balanced equation and the catalyst used in the Haber process: equation: $3H_2 + N_2 \rightarrow 2NH_3$ catalyst: iron.

Question		Answer	Hint
b)			When drawing diagrams like this, ensure that the bonding electrons are on the line or within the overlapped area. The answer shown demonstrates the variations of the bonding electrons that are accepted. You must also ensure that you have included the symbols of the elements involved.
c)	(i)	Both axes labelled with units (1 mark) Both scales correct (1 mark) Graph drawn accurately (1 mark) (points must be plotted correctly and line drawn, either by joining the dots or by a smooth curve or curve of best fit) The line must be drawn from the origin.	When drawing any graph ensure that: ■ the graph is bigger than half the size of the graph paper given ■ all the labels and units are correct ■ all points are correctly plotted including 0,0 (the origin) if it is included in the table; which in this case it is not.
	(ii)	93–94	Percentage of ammonia produced shows a steady increase of around 13/14% each time the pressure is doubled.
d)	(i)	Potassium	Nitrogen, potassium and phosphorus are the essential nutrients required for healthy plant growth.

Question			Answer	Hint
		(ii)	28.2%	**Worked answer:**
				Step 1: Calculate the gram formula mass of ammonium phosphate using the formula $(NH_4)_3PO_4$ $((14 \times 3) + (1 \times 4 \times 3) + (31 \times 1) + (16 \times 4) = 149)$.
				Step 2: Calculate the mass of nitrogen in the compound. Each molecule contains three nitrogen atoms so the mass of nitrogen in the compound is $3 \times 14 = 42$.
				Step 3: Calculate the percentage by mass using the following equation, which is on page 1 of your data booklet:
				% by mass $= \dfrac{m}{GFM} \times 100 = \dfrac{42 \times 100}{149} = 28.2\%$
5			**Open-ended question** 3 marks: The candidate has demonstrated a good conceptual understanding of the chemistry involved. 2 marks: The candidate has demonstrated a reasonable understanding of the chemistry involved. 1 mark: The candidate has demonstrated a limited understanding of the chemistry involved. 0 marks: The candidate has demonstrated no understanding of the chemistry that is relevant to the problem/situation. The candidate has made no statement(s) that is/are relevant to the problem/situation.	Open-ended questions have no single correct answer. Listed below are **some** of the options that may be included and explained in your answer. **This list is not exhaustive and you do not have to include all of these to gain the full 3 marks.** Ensure that what you have included has been explained fully and clearly. Include diagrams, equations, etc. that may help with your explanation. ■ Redox: oxidation (loss of electrons) and reduction (gain of electrons). ■ Ions achieving stable electron arrangements: formation of ions, full energy levels (noble gas arrangement), ionic bonding. ■ Cells: reactivity series, direction of electron flow, electrolyte, voltage.
6	a)	(i)	Uranium or U or $^{234}_{92}U$	The atomic number and mass number are not required as the question simply asks you to identify element X, but if you did give them, then they must be correct. The numbers on both sides of the equation must balance.

Question			Answer	Hint
		(ii)	The alpha radiation cannot pass through the titanium case of the pacemaker	Alpha radiation has very low penetrating power and can be stopped by paper or a few centimetres of air and so the titanium case of the pacemaker would not allow the radiation to pass through it, protecting the patient.
	b)		0.2 g	**Worked answer:** Time in use = 25 years Original mass = 0.8 Half-life = 90 years Using the formula provided: $\frac{25 \times 0.8}{90} = 0.2\,g$
7	a)		Esters	Esters contain the 'ester link' which can be identified by the –COO– functional group.
	b)	(i)	Hydroxyl functional group	It is important to learn the names and be able to identify all of the functional groups. As part of your revision, it is good practice to create a table listing all the homologous series and their functional groups.
		(ii)		When drawing the full structural formula of any compound, always ensure that each element has formed the correct number of bonds: ■ carbon – four bonds ■ hydrogen – one bond ■ oxygen – two bonds. You must also ensure that ■ all bonds are shown ■ all symbols are correct ■ the bond from the 'C' goes to the 'O' of the 'OH' and not the 'H'.
	c)		Bromine solution would be decolourised.	An addition reaction would occur between the double carbon-to-carbon bond of the oils and the bromine solution resulting in the bromine solution turning from brown/orange to colourless.
8	a)		Neutralisation	The hydrochloric acid would react with the magnesium hydroxide (an alkali) in a neutralisation reaction to produce the salt magnesium chloride, and water.

Question			Answer	Hint
	b)	**(i)**	$Mg^{2+} + 2Cl^- \rightarrow 2Cl + Mg$	The equation containing chlorine must be multiplied by two so that there are two electrons in each equation before they are combined. The electrons then cancel each other out and so are not included in the final answer.
		(ii)	Ions are free to move	Ionic compounds conduct when molten or in solution because the ions are free to move.
	c)			The chlorine produced can be recycled back into the process. The answer you have drawn must be directional, i.e. have an arrow head to show that it is going from the products up toward the chlorine for Stage 2.
9	**a)**			Markers assess these questions by asking, 'would this work as drawn?'
	b)		8.8 g	**Worked answer:** Step 1: Establish the molar ratio from the balanced equation. 1 mole of C_2H_5OH reacts to produce 2 moles of CO_2. Step 2: Calculate the moles of C_2H_5OH using, moles = mass ÷ gram formula mass $(4.6 ÷ 46 = 0.1)$. (The gram formula mass of C_2H_5OH is $(2 × 12) + (5 × 1) + 16 + 1 = 46$ g.) Step 3: Use the ratio to establish the moles of carbon dioxide produced $(0.1 × 2 = 0.2$ moles of CO_2 produced). Step 4: Calculate the mass of CO_2 produced using, mass = moles × formula mass $(0.2 × 44 = 8.8$ g). (The gram formula mass of CO_2 is $(12 + (2 × 16)) = 44$ g.)

Question			Answer	Hint
	c)		Exothermic	
10	a)		Electrons are free to move (ions is not accepted here)	All metals conduct electricity because they have electrons that are free to move, i.e. they are delocalised. In an ionic compound, it is the ions that allow them to conduct when molten or in solution but metal elements are made up of atoms not ions.
	b)		$Cu + Cl_2 \rightarrow CuCl_2$	Remember that chlorine is diatomic and must be represented as Cl_2. Always check that your formulae are correct.
	c)	(i)	Ores	Metals are extracted from ores unless they are very unreactive such as gold.
		(ii)	Reduction	Reduction is the gain of electrons and the copper ions must gain electrons to form copper atoms.
11	a)		Neutralisation	Vinegar is an acidic solution and limescale is a carbonate and so a neutralisation reaction would occur between the two.
	b)	(i)	$10.0\,cm^3$	The rough or first titration value should not be included in the average calculation.
		(ii)	$0.25\,mol\,l^{-1}$	**Worked answer:** Step 1: Establish the molar ratio. 1 mole of NaOH reacts with 1 mole of CH_3COOH. Step 2: Calculate the number of moles of NaOH by using $N = C \times V$ ($0.5 \times 10/1000 = 0.005$ moles). Step 3: Use the ratio to establish the moles of CH_3COOH reacted and because the ratio is one to one, then the number of moles of CH_3COOH reacted is 0.005 moles. Step 4: Calculate the concentration of CH_3COOH using, $C = N \div V = 0.005 \div 20/1000 = 0.25\,mol\,l^{-1}$
12	a)	(i)	Temperature or concentration	Particle size would not be accepted here because the H_2O_2 is a liquid.
		(ii)	It has a large surface area	The smaller the particle size, the larger the surface area; this increases the efficiency of a catalyst.

Question			Answer	Hint
	b)	**(i)**	$0.33\,cm^3\,s^{-1}$	Rate = change in quantity/change in time Rate = $\dfrac{15}{45}$ = 0.33 This is a unit question and so the unit must be given correctly to gain the second mark.
		(ii)	The concentration of the reactant is decreasing/being used up.	As the reaction proceeds, the concentration of reactants is reduced and so the rate slows until the reaction stops.
13	**a)**		Addition	The monomer ethene is unsaturated and so the type of polymerisation that takes place is addition.
	b)	**(i)**		The polymer must contain six carbon atoms, two for each monomer. It must also show both end bonds to indicate that this is a section of a polymer.
		(ii)	Removes the double bonds of the ethene monomers, preventing further reactions	The hydrogen would add across the carbon-to-carbon double bond of the ethene monomers preventing addition polymerisation from taking place.